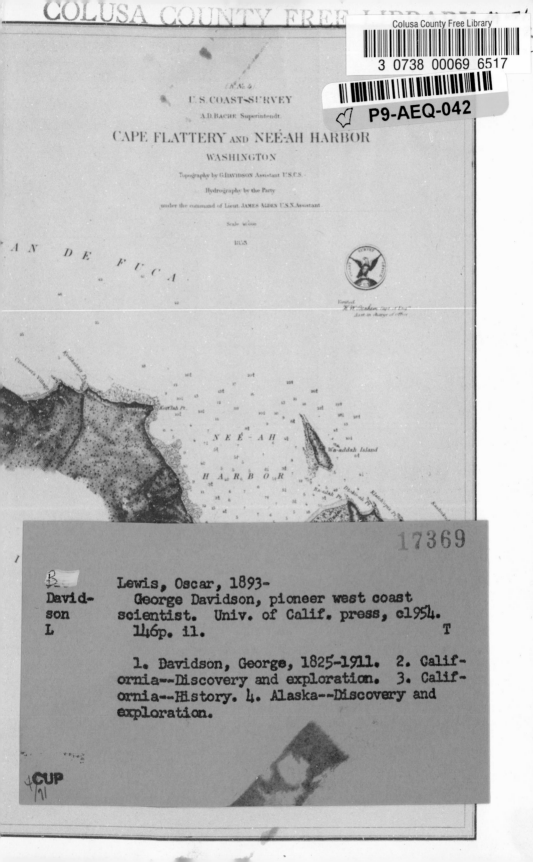

[N. 4]

U.S.COAST-SURVEY

A.D.BACHE Superintendt.

CAPE FLATTERY AND NEÉ-AH HARBOR

WASHINGTON

Topography by G.DAVIDSON Assistant U.S.C.S.

Hydrography by the Party

under the command of Lieut. JAMES ALDEN U.S.N.Assistant

Scale 10.000

1853

AN DE FUCA

NEÉ-AH

HARBOR

Wa-addah Island

17369

Lewis, Oscar, 1893-
   George Davidson, pioneer west coast
scientist. Univ. of Calif. press, c1954.
  146p. il.   T

   1. Davidson, George, 1825-1911. 2. Calif-
ornia--Discovery and exploration. 3. Calif-
ornia--History. 4. Alaska--Discovery and
exploration.

CUP

GEORGE DAVIDSON · pioneer west coast scientist

BERKELEY AND LOS ANGELES

GEORGE DAVIDSON

• pioneer west coast scientist

OSCAR LEWIS

UNIVERSITY OF CALIFORNIA PRESS, 1954

University of California Press
Berkeley and Los Angeles, California

Cambridge University Press
London, England

Library of Congress Catalog Card Number: 54–7628
Printed in the United States of America
By the University of California Printing Department
Designed by Marion Jackson

· preface

Although George Davidson during by far the greater part of his more than sixty years of professional life was closely identified with scientific activities on the Pacific Coast and throughout most of that period occupied a position of leadership in his chosen field, the preëminent part he played in the advancement of our knowledge of the geography of the area, and of the history of early exploration of its shoreline, is virtually unknown to the general public today.

In the half century that has passed since his death, Davidson's highly valuable contributions to geodesy, astronomy, and allied sciences, and to the history of the first navigators to visit the coast, have been almost completely forgotten. Yet during much of his lifetime he was acknowledged to be one of the most eminent scientists of his day and a leading spirit in the beginnings of organized scientific research in the West.

His present-day obscurity—which in view of his notable accomplishments is clearly undeserved—is due in part to the fact that but little was written about him, either in his lifetime or later, and that such summaries of his life and works as found their way into print appeared mainly in the publications of scientific societies or in other journals of limited circulation. After his death in 1911, obituaries were published in the newspapers of San Francisco and other coast cities, and resumés of his career appeared in a number of publications, including the *University of California Chronicle*, the *Transactions* of the American Society of Civil Engineers, the *Bulle-*

tin of the American Geographical Society, and the *Proceedings* of the California Academy of Sciences. These, together with brief sketches in *Who's Who in America* and the *Dictionary of American Biography*, and a longer paper by Henry R. Wagner in the December, 1932, *Quarterly* of the California Historical Society, about exhaust the list.

In the preparation of the present work, these sources, along with a number of others of less importance, have been consulted. The author's main reliance, however, has been on the extensive collection of Davidson's personal papers in the Bancroft Library at the University of California, Berkeley; on his official correspondence in the National Archives and in the Library of the U. S. Coast and Geodetic Survey in Washington, D.C.; and on the books and manuscript material at the California Academy of Sciences in San Francisco.

In addition, some useful data were gleaned from the collections of the Historical Society of Pennsylvania in Philadelphia, the American Geographical Society in New York, and the California State Library in Sacramento, as well as those at the Society of California Pioneers and the California Historical Society in San Francisco, and the San Francisco Public Library.

For their valuable help and suggestions, the author makes grateful acknowledgment to Mrs. Eleanor Bancroft, Miss Edith Cadell, Mrs. Florence Chessé, J. S. Cook, Richard H. Dillon, Francis P. Farquhar, Mrs. Helen S. Giffen, Patrick D. Goldsworthy, Erwin G. Gudde, George P. Hammond, Captain Thomas J. Maher, Mrs. Edna M. Parratt, Miss Sybil Power-Kent, Miss Veronica J. Sexton, Joseph R. Slevin, Wyland Stanley, and Rear Admiral Robert F. A. Studds.

· contents

. illustrations

I · childhood and youth

George Davidson was born in Notting-
ham, England, on May 9, 1825. His father, Thomas Davidson,
a native of Arbroath, a seaport and industrial town in Scotland,
was the son of a prosperous textile manufacturer and owner of a
mill that produced sailcloth. George Davidson's mother was the
former Janet Drummond, daughter of John Drummond of the
near-by fishing and manufacturing village of Montrose.

Soon after their marriage, his parents moved to Nottingham,
where the father, said to be a man of "strong mechanical inclinations," planned to engage in the manufacture of machine-made
lace. This venture seems to have been an outgrowth of experiments carried on by Thomas Davidson's father, the Arbroath
sailcloth manufacturer. His grandson, the subject of this sketch,
once wrote that he possessed samples of his grandfather's lace,
which he described as "very fine" in quality, and added that he
believed it to be the first ever made by machinery.

It was at the lacemaking center of Nottingham that young
Davidson spent his first seven years. In one of his later writings
he recalled a few of his childhood memories of that period. His
mother, whom he described as "a woman of great force of character," undertook his education, and taught him to such good
effect that he was able to read the New Testament by the time
he was four. "Later," he added, "when the increasing family
[which presently numbered nine—four boys and five girls] demanded all her time, I was sent for a few months to a Dame's

school; all I recollect is the old Dame and her cap . . . and the children having to stand in the corner wearing dunce-caps."

The mother had a deep interest in, and a considerable knowledge of, the principles of mechanics—surely an uncommon avocation for women of the period—and young George, the eldest child, recalled her demonstrating to him by simple experiments certain basic principles of leverage, the force of steam, and similar phenomena. This obviously made a lasting impression on him, for nearly seventy years later he expressed his regret that he had failed to develop as fully as he might have the interest in mechanical theory and practice that had been awakened in him when he was hardly out of his infancy. He then stated that he had ever since "profoundly regretted" that he "did not keep true to his mechanical instincts."

The elder Davidson's lacemaking venture at Nottingham could not have been very successful, for the son, in his reminiscence of the period, wrote of his mother's indomitable fortitude in the face of adversity. He recalled, too, that on winter days when he set off for school he lacked a coat and carried in his hand a newly baked potato as a means of warding off the biting cold.

Then, in 1832, when George was seven, Thomas Davidson set out with his family for the United States, crossing the Atlantic as thousands of his countrymen were doing each year in the expectation of bettering their lot in the new land. The group took passage on the sailing ship *John Wells*, a former whaler that had been converted into an emigrant vessel and fitted with accommodations—of a sort—for forty passengers. "My father had many cases of goods," wrote the son in his only reference to the voyage, "and I remember my mother's very big red chest, which carried all the household linen, most of which she had herself spun."

It was Thomas Davidson's intention to set up a lacemaking factory in Philadelphia, and probably the "many cases of goods" mentioned above contained equipment and materials to be used in that venture. But this, too, ended in failure, one reason being, according to the son, that it proved impossible to find in the city workmen sufficiently skilled to set up and operate the complicated lace looms. Another reason seems to have been that the demand for machine-made lace was less than had been expected. At any rate, the whole project was abandoned. Reading between the lines of the son's account, however, one gathers that perhaps the main reason for failure lay in Thomas Davidson's lack of those qualities necessary to the successful conduct of such an enterprise. "Father," wrote he, "had strong mechanical inclinations but never developed them to any business issue."

Young George entered the public schools of Philadelphia and in due course passed the entrance examinations for admission to the Central High School, which had recently been founded and was destined to occupy an important place in the city's educational system for many years to come. His connection with that school proved a fortunate one, for the associations formed there played a decisive part in shaping his future career. Heading the Central High School faculty was a young man named Alexander Dallas Bache, who some fifteen years earlier had graduated from West Point and at the time George met him was an important figure in educational circles, both as an administrator and as a scholar in the fields of physics, astronomy, and geodesy.

For Bache, young Davidson early developed an admiration and a respect that were to persist and grow stronger with the passage of the years, and that presently led to a close friendship and professional association that continued unbroken until the elder man's death more than a quarter century later. Nor was this admiration all one-sided, for Professor Bache seems to have early recognized in the young student qualities of a high order and to have neglected no opportunity to fire his ambition and direct his studies into productive channels. Davidson himself, years later, gave grateful recognition of his mentor's services in this connection by stating that although the whole bent of his mind was toward "mechanics of the higher order, combined with

mathematics," his original intention had been to fit himself for
a professorship of the classics, where these qualities would, of
course, have been of little practical value.

An event that was to mark an important turning point in his
career—although there is little likelihood that he realized it at
the time—took place only a year or two before Davidson en-
rolled at the Central High School. In 1840 a wealthy Phila-
delphian, George M. Justice, presented the school with a telescope
and other astronomical equipment, thereby enabling Bache to
set up what is said to have been the first magnetic observatory
in the United States. Soon after Davidson became a student at
the school, he was appointed one of the student assistants at the
observatory, and by taking the position he entered a field of
scientific research that was to be a major concern for well over
sixty years. From 1843 until he was graduated two years later,
he was engaged in astronomical work under Bache's direction,
first at the observatory of the high school and later at that of
the newly founded Girard College. He was appointed magnetic
observer of the college in 1844 and remained in charge of night
observations there throughout the remainder of his student life.

It was in that period that he first revealed the physical endurance and the prodigious capacity for work that were to stir the
wonder of his associates as long as he lived. He himself once
stated that throughout the next three years he averaged no more
than three hours' sleep out of the twenty-four, and that he was
absent from his classes and observation work only twice—both
times because of illness. In addition to keeping up his studies
to such good purpose that he usually stood at or near the head
of his class in scholarship, and his nightly work at the observatory, he was able to crowd in a variety of other activities, in spite
of the fact that he daily walked from his home to school, a distance of nine miles.

In later years he recalled one of these extracurricular assignments. When Bache presently left Central High School to accept

the chair of chemistry and natural philosophy at the University of Pennsylvania, he called on his young assistant for help in preparing for his teaching duties there. Davidson thereupon, in his own words, "worked five or six hours after school for nine months in Professor Bache's library making drawings to illustrate his lectures, computing tables, etc."

This, however, was but an early manifestation of a characteristic that was to remain strong throughout the years. All his life Davidson was proud of his physical stamina—of a capacity for sustained work that rarely failed to impress acquaintances at all stages of his career. In 1900, when he was seventy-five, he wrote: "In fifty years of official life I took less than fifty days leave of absence and worked every holiday and Sunday for forty-five years of that time. And I continue ceaselessly to work because I love it, because I have the constitution to stand it, and because I believe that I can add something to human knowledge and especially to benefit the young."

Upon his graduation from Central High School on July 15, 1845—he was then two months past twenty—he was valedictorian of his class. However, in order to deliver his address— which bore the significant title "The Progress of Science"—it was necessary for him to return to the school from the New England coast; he had joined the United States Coast Survey a month earlier and was already on duty in the field.

II · the u. s. coast survey

The agency of which Davidson thus became a part was one of the federal government's oldest scientific bureaus, its establishment having first been proposed by President Jefferson in the early 1800's. On February 10, 1807, Congress duly passed the necessary legislation. This, entitled "An Act to Provide for Surveying the Coasts of the United States," authorized the President "to cause a survey to be taken . . . in which shall be designated the islands and shoals, with the roads or places of anchorage, within twenty leagues of any part of the shores of the United States; and also the respective courses and distances between the principal capes, or head lands, together with such other matters as he may deem proper for completing an accurate chart of every part of the coasts."

The act also provided that, in order to get this project under way, the President cause "proper and intelligent persons to be employed," that "such public vessels . . . as he may judge expedient" be assigned to the survey, and that a sum "not exceeding fifty thousand dollars" of public funds be appropriated to inaugurate the work.

In order to organize the new bureau—which was known at first as the "Survey of the Coast"—and to permit it to begin functioning, letters of inquiry were sent to a group of the country's leading scientists, asking advice on how the work could best be accomplished and inviting them to suggest men well qualified to undertake it. As a result of these recommendations, President Jefferson presently selected as the first head of the Survey Ferdinand R. Hassler, an engineer who, after a distinguished professional career in his native Switzerland, was a teacher of mathematics at West Point.

However, because of unsettled conditions both at home and abroad, little of a practical nature was accomplished for a considerable number of years. The precision instruments necessary for making accurate surveys being unavailable in this country, Hassler was sent to Europe in 1811, charged with "contracting for the purchase and the supervision of the construction of the apparatus." The War of 1812 broke out while he was abroad, and it was not until 1815 that he completed his mission and returned. Further long delays ensued, for although some tentative surveys were made in 1816, Congress presently repealed the 1807 act, and it was not until 1832 that a new appropriation was passed, which permitted the work to be resumed.

Thus it was close to a quarter century after the project had first been authorized that the much-needed task of safeguarding the growing commerce of the nation by providing dependable surveys and charts of its shoreline got actively under way. The work, which now proceeded under Hassler's direction until his death eleven years later, although technically above criticism, was conducted in a way that aroused resentment in many quarters. For Hassler, although an able and conscientious engineer, was a man of uncommonly strong opinions and prejudices. One cause of resentment was that he thought so little of the scientific attainments of Americans that the men he employed to work on the Survey were almost exclusively those with European training. The result, it is said, is that one rarely encountered a member of his staff who spoke English without a strong foreign accent.

One instance of his brusque and autocratic behavior survives. He strode one day into the office of the Secretary of the Treasury— the Survey then being under that department—and demanded an increase in salary, naming a sum far larger than he was then receiving. The Secretary protested, pointing out that the amount he wished was more than he himself was paid. Hassler retorted: "Suppose it is! Any President can create a Secretary of the Treasury. But only God can make a Hassler!"

The man selected to succeed the able but undiplomatic Hassler was of a quite different background and temperament. This was Alexander Dallas Bache, who had been principal of Philadelphia's Central High School while Davidson was a student there, and later professor of chemistry and natural philosophy at the University of Pennsylvania.

Until the time the new superintendent was placed in charge in 1843, the Survey had confined its activities mainly to the states bordering on the Atlantic, having begun with the Long Island

and Connecticut shores and gradually extended up and down the coast. At first the objective had been, in Hassler's words, "to make a complete triangulation survey of the whole coast including the determination of latitude, longitude, and azimuths of the principal places, and bases measured with the greatest possible accuracy."

In the mid-1830's the topographical work of the land parties had been supplemented by hydrographic surveys of the offshore waters, the brig *Washington*, the first of a long line of Coast Survey vessels, being assigned to that duty in 1837. From 1834 onward, charts embodying the findings of the Survey were issued by the bureau for the guidance of navigators, and in 1842 the first chart of New York Harbor and its approaches was published. This was a copperplate engraving, the Survey having recently added a printing press to its equipment.

In the first half of the nineteenth century, by successive additions to the nation's territory, the length of its coastline had been more than doubled. The Louisiana Purchase and the acquisition of Florida and Texas had added many hundreds of miles of land bordering on the Gulf of Mexico, and the conquest of California in the late 1840's extended the country's domain to the shores of the Pacific.

Therefore when Professor Bache assumed direction of the work in 1843, the Survey faced the necessity of greatly extending the scope of its operations. As a result of his persuasions, soon after he took office Congress increased substantially the bureau's appropriations, and he organized new parties and dispatched them to the south to make reconnaissance surveys of the shores of the Gulf from Florida to Texas. It was in that area, as well as along the New England coast, that young Davidson had his first experiences in field work. For Bache, upon taking office, had promptly offered his former student a berth as "clerk and computer to the Superintendent"; and Davidson—who was still in school—as promptly accepted, though it was mutually agreed that he would not enter on his new duties until after his graduation.

Davidson's first months with the Survey were evidently not altogether happy ones. Sitting behind a desk and performing routine tasks was ever irksome to a person of his abundant energies. Moreover, he seems to have found the Washington of that day thoroughly uncongenial, for in his letters of the period he frequently referred to it as "Washington D(reary) C(ity)." The consequence was that after a few months he asked to be assigned to duty in the field. This request was presently granted, and for the next several years he was almost constantly on the move, spending the winter months with survey crews mapping the coasts of the southern states fronting on the Atlantic and the Gulf, and dividing his summers between New Harmony, Indiana—where he worked up his notes—and New England—where he served as an astronomical observer with the superintendent's party.

During his field work in the South he gained his first practical experience in the profession he was to follow for more than fifty years. For the parties to which he was attached were engaged in reconnaissance, triangulation, latitude and longitude observations, field magnetics, and other computations necessary for the preparation of detailed and accurate charts of the area. Moreover, during much of that time he was a member of a party led by Robert H. Fauntleroy, a brilliant engineer then on the staff of the Survey, and—as we shall presently see—the acquaintance thus begun was to have an important bearing on his future.

III · first years
on the west coast

During the period from 1845 to 1850,
events of great consequence were taking place on the far edge
of the continent. Mexico's faltering grasp on California and that
territory's annexation by the United States, followed soon after
by the discovery of gold in the Sierra foothills, set off one of the
greatest mass migrations in history.

These developments made imperative a prompt further extension of the work of the Coast Survey. Superintendent Bache
foresaw that the world-wide interest aroused by news of the gold
discovery would result in a vast increase in water-borne commerce, and this would necessitate the accurate mapping of the
Pacific shoreline and the installation of numerous aids to
navigation. With hundreds of ships converging on San Francisco
from every corner of the globe, the need for such safeguards
was both clear and urgent. For at the time California passed to
the control of the United States there were no lighthouses, buoys,
or other markings anywhere on the long coastline from San
Diego to Puget Sound, and such charts as existed were few and
of almost no practical value.

The result was that the gold ships arrived with whatever charts
could be found in the ports where the voyages had originated.
Davidson himself later stated that many of the ships had nothing
more to guide them than maps taken from school atlases. Others,
a bit more fortunate, used charts printed in England that were

based on the exploratory surveys made by Captain George Vancouver on his visit to the coast more than half a century earlier.
So far as is known, the only available chart of San Francisco
Bay and its narrow entrance—toward which virtually all the
gold ships were headed—was that made in the mid-1820's by
another English exploring party, commanded by Captain William Beechey. However, a few of the ships from the east coast
of the United States may have carried charts prepared by members of the Wilkes expedition, which had visited the area more
recently—that is, in 1841.

Faced by this emergency, the seriousness of which was demon-
strated by reports of frequent wrecks on the coast, Superintendent
Bache lost no time in laying plans for beginning a survey of the
area. Accordingly, as early as October, 1848, he dispatched the
Coast Survey schooner *Ewing* to California and assigned a U. S.
Navy lieutenant, William P. McArthur, to command her, with
instructions to begin a hydrographic survey. However, by the
time the *Ewing* was fitted out and had journeyed round the Horn,
the greater part of a year had gone by, and the vessel did not
arrive until mid-September, 1849.

By that time the gold rush was at its height, and Lieutenant
McArthur discovered that, with the inflated values then prevailing
throughout California, it was impossible to hire men to operate
the craft at the modest wages he was authorized to pay. The
result was that the *Ewing* was sent to the Sandwich Islands in
the hope of signing on a crew. That mission proving unsuccessful,
the ship returned to San Francisco early in 1850. There a crew
was finally assembled, and the *Ewing* sailed north on April 3
to make a survey of the entrance to the Columbia River.

During the next few months the *Ewing* worked its way southward. The result of the findings on that voyage was the publication by the Survey late that year of a three-sheet reconnaissance
chart extending from San Diego to the entrance to the Columbia
River. In September, 1850, Lieutenant McArthur was ordered

back to Washington to take command of a newly commissioned Survey steamer that had been built for further hydrographic work on the coast. On the voyage from San Francisco to the Isthmus, however, he fell victim to one of the epidemics then frequent on the crowded coast-to-coast steamers and died as the vessel entered Panama harbor.

In the meantime, Superintendent Bache was busily laying further plans designed to speed the survey of the far-western waters. In the summer of 1849, preparations were made to dispatch to the coast a land-based party charged with carrying on surveys in coöperation with the hydrographic work being done by Lieutenant McArthur. Young Davidson seems to have been one of those designated to join this group; several of his letters of the period make reference to plans for his imminent departure for California and to last-minute preparations he was making for the voyage. However, Congress failed to appropriate the necessary funds, and the project had to be temporarily abandoned. This development must have been a sharp disappointment to Davidson. Years later he confessed that "all through 1848 and 1849" he had had the "California fever" in its most virulent form, although for many months he had concealed that fact from his chief.

The hoped-for opportunity was, however, soon to come, and in one respect the change of plans proved fortunate. For when at length the party set out, Davidson went not in a subordinate capacity but as its leader. The group, which was charged with determining the positions of headlands, capes, and other prominent geographical features of the shoreline, was made up of Davidson and three young assistants, James S. Lawson, A. S. Harrison, and John Rockwell, all members of the Coast Survey staff, who had volunteered for the work. The party left the east coast late in May, 1850, on board the steamer *Philadelphia*, and crossed the Isthmus of Panama early in June. On the west coast they embarked on the *Tennessee* and landed in San Francisco on June 19.

Because all during that period the funds available for the Survey's work were strictly limited, all four members of the party had agreed not only to serve for a year at the same wage they had received in the East but to do whatever manual work might be necessary, for it was realized that—as Lieutenant McArthur had earlier learned—it would be impossible to hire helpers on the west coast without exceeding the authorized budget.

Their salaries were indeed moderate as compared with those prevailing in California at the time, when the going rate for unskilled laborers was $10 a day, and mechanics and members of the building trades often received twice that sum. As chief, Davidson's remuneration was $900 a year, out of which he was obliged to pay his own living expenses; his three assistants received $30 a month, plus an allowance for food and shelter. Long afterward, in recalling that period, Davidson wrote that while in the field in California in the early 1850's, he, as head of the group, earned $75 per month, and "the most valuable man in the party—the cook" received exactly twice that sum.

This, however, was a matter of no great consequence to him, for throughout his career the matter of salary—though he by no means ignored it—was ever subordinate to that of doing interesting and important work in his chosen field. And the California of the time presented opportunities that appealed strongly to his professional instincts. Moreover, he was in direct charge of his party, and since headquarters in Washington were so far away, his responsibilities were correspondingly heavy—a circumstance that he found more pleasant than otherwise. "My instructions were in elaborate detail," he later wrote, "through thirty or forty pages, with the last saving sentence that if none of the proposed schemes could be carried out I was to do the best that my judgment suggested."

There is ample evidence that during his first years on the coast Davidson frequently had to decide when and how the work assigned to him should be carried out. The over-all purpose of the survey was, as stated, to prepare accurate and detailed charts of the coastline from the Mexican border to Puget Sound. To speed this work, two groups were now put in the field, to each of which was assigned a separate part of the operation. That of a hydrographic nature—the charting of the water areas, including bays, rivers, and inlets; the determination of depths, channels, currents, and the like—was placed in charge of Lieutenant James Alden, a naval officer then stationed on the coast, who had been a member of the Wilkes expedition some nine years earlier.

The first function of Davidson's party was, by working in coördination with Lieutenant Alden's group, to determine by astronomical observations the true positions of the more prominent headlands on the coast, specifically Points Conception, Pinos, and Loma in California and Cape Disappointment at the mouth of the Columbia River. Moreover, because the already published McArthur charts fixed the longitude of San Francisco and other coastal points at the locations determined by Wilkes in 1841, it was necessary in the subsequent printings to check their accuracy and correct any errors that might be discovered.

Thus during their first three and a half months in the field, Davidson and his party were engaged in this work, mainly at Point Conception, some forty miles to the northwest of Santa Barbara and the most conspicuous landfall on the southern coast. Then, early in 1851, the survey was continued northward, Davidson and Lawson, using the *Ewing* as a base of operations, proceeding up the coast, with frequent stops en route, as far as the Columbia River. After this reconnaissance, Davidson returned to San Francisco to write up his findings and prepare his reports.

As a result of their first eighteen months of work, during which Davidson and his aides were almost continuously in the field, the Survey published the following year charts of Point Conception and Point Pinos, of the bays of Trinidad, Humboldt, San Francisco, and San Diego, and of the mouth of the Columbia. All these were of course highly useful to the masters of ships engaged in the then active maritime traffic on the coast, for during the 1850's the number of ships plying these waters was far greater than at any time since.

In addition to his primary task of fixing the longitude and latitude of prominent coastal bays and headlands, Davidson was given a second assignment: to recommend suitable locations for lighthouses, another important navigational aid. Accordingly, in his reports to Washington in the first half-dozen years, there are frequently references not only to that subject but to a variety of more or less related matters: meteorological observations, notes on currents, shipwrecks, the volume of commerce at certain ports, and much else.

That the work he and his party were engaged in during those pioneer years entailed much hardship—and a considerable degree of danger—is clear from the nature of their duties. For they were engaged in making the first detailed surveys of a coastline that over much of its length was rugged in the extreme, with few harbors or inlets where safe landings could be made, and where the little survey ship, exploring waters close inshore, faced an ever-present danger from submerged reefs and other navigational hazards.

Davidson and his aides fully shared these perils, for although their duties consisted mainly in making land surveys and observations, they traveled from point to point on board the Survey's ship, going ashore from time to time and setting up stations on headlands or other elevated spots. This involved their landing, with all their equipment and supplies, in small boats, frequently on rocky shores where unskillful handling of their little craft might well have brought disaster, for the piloting of such small vessels through the surf onto an unknown shore has long been looked on as one of the most hazardous of all feats of seamanship.

In the early and middle 1850's, Davidson and his helpers performed that difficult maneuver not once or twice but scores of times; in fact, he once stated that in his first three years on the coast he made "more than forty" such landings. Although he and others of his party escaped major mishaps while so engaged, every member of the group invariably was soaked to the skin in the process of making shore and carrying their instruments and provisions to the beach. Probably as a result of these frequent drenchings, Davidson contracted rheumatism, from which he was to suffer intermittently for more than two decades.

However, not all members of the Survey staff on the coast got off so lightly. In October, 1852, a member of the staff, Assistant Joseph S. Ruth, with whom Davidson had formed a close friendship when both were stationed at the Washington headquarters, was drowned off the mouth of the Columbia River by the capsizing of the small boat in which he was going ashore. Later, the boat of James Lawson, one of Davidson's assistants, was swamped at the mouth of Tomales Bay, a few miles north of San Francisco; however, Lawson managed not only to get safely ashore but to salvage most of the instruments and supplies the craft carried.

But landing through the surf was not the only hazard Davidson and his companions were called on to face. In his report to Superintendent Bache, written from Astoria, Oregon Territory, in the same month his friend Ruth met his death, and published in the Coast Survey *Report* for 1852, Davidson makes clear that he and his group were sometimes in imminent danger of attack by hostile Indians. A month or two earlier the party had landed to make a topographical survey of Tatersh Island, a small, steep-sided body of land, to which, he stated, the Indians of the area "resort in summer about one hundred and fifty strong."

He stated that the survey work there "has been executed at the risk of the life of every one at work on it. The only means of conveyance I could furnish," he continued, "was two small canoes, which were forced to land on the rocks and rocky points. . . . I consider the station to have been occupied at very great risk from the hostility of the Indians; but a knowledge that we were always prepared for an attack, without doubt, prevented one. We built a breastwork, and could fire sixty rounds without reloading. Guard was kept six hours every night."

Davidson's report from Astoria is interesting from another angle, for it reveals that even that early he had already embarked on a campaign he was to wage for many years—that of preserving so far as practicable the native Indian names of geographical features of the coast. "I have," he wrote his chief, "designated my last station as at 'Scarborough Harbor,' from Wilkes; but the name on the English charts is Nee'ah bay, which is the Indian name for bay: I would therefore propose to call it Neeah bay, . . . and if you think it right, could have a note to that effect entered on the records." Clearly that suggestion was followed, for the inlet, lying just inside the entrance to the Strait of Juan de Fuca on its southern shore, today bears that name, although the spelling has been shortened to Neah Bay.

The hardships and dangers of life in the field were, however, no drawback to one of young Davidson's temperament; indeed, during his many years with the Survey he made no secret of the fact that he found active work in the open much more congenial than the supervising of such operations from behind a desk at headquarters. The consequence was that throughout his career he seldom passed up an opportunity to join any expedition organized for scientific purposes, regardless of how remote or inaccessible its destination might be. So widely did he travel on such missions that in 1900 he wrote proudly that on such official tasks he had covered a total of 402,188 miles, a distance of more than sixteen times round the world. In a letter to the editor of the *National Geographic Magazine*, written that same year, referring to his more than half century of active field work he stated: "I made it a rule to volunteer for every difficult, disagreeable and far-away work that was projected, and usually managed to succeed in getting it."

IV · new harmony

Soon after he went to Washington in 1846, Davidson made the acquaintance of a man who, like Alexander Bache, was to influence strongly the course of his subsequent career. This was Robert H. Fauntleroy, a civil engineer in his early forties who had recently joined the Survey. A native of Greenville, Virginia, and the son of a prosperous slave-owning planter, Fauntleroy was left an orphan at the age of thirteen. He remained in Virginia until the early 1830's; then, having, it is said, grown convinced of the moral injustice, as well as the economic weaknesses, of the institution of slavery, he moved northward and joined a cousin in the operation of a mercantile store at New Harmony, Indiana.

This village, originally called Harmony, in the extreme southwest corner of the state and fronting on the Wabash, was then much in the public eye, for it was the locale of one of the most picturesque of many socialistic land colonies then being organized in various parts of the country. Founded in 1814 by a group of German emigrants led by one George Rapp and terming themselves the Economists, the colony functioned there for some ten years. Then its property, consisting of 30,000 acres of fertile farming land, passed into other hands when Rapp and his followers moved to central Pennsylvania and established a second colony, which they called Economy.

The purchaser of the Harmony property was Robert Owen, a wealthy owner of textile mills in the town of New Lanark,

Scotland. Owen had won international renown by the then un-precedented measures he had taken to better the lot of his em-ployees through reducing their working hours, conferring other social and economic benefits on them, and abolishing child labor in his factories. Having failed in his efforts to persuade other manufacturers to follow his example, Owen embarked on a career as writer and lecturer in an attempt to further his liberal and humanitarian views. It was, it is said, due mainly to his influence that England enacted its first laws shortening the work-ing hours of factory hands and limiting the hiring of children.

These measures, however, were far less drastic than Owen had been advocating. In an effort to prove that his theories were prac-tical he organized and financed a number of coöperative groups in various parts of England in which the workers were to share in the profits of the ventures. Undeterred by the fact that these socialistic experiments in the homeland uniformly ended in failure—mainly because of the competition of privately owned factories, he maintained—Owen turned his eyes toward the New World and in 1824 bought the Rappites' property in Indiana.

Owen's New Harmony colony was unique among such proj-ects in that from the beginning it was planned as a center where research in the field of science and technical knowledge would be fostered and made available to lighten the labors of the col-onists, and it was intended to set an example for workers else-where. Associated with Owen in this work was an eminent geologist, William Maclure; and Maclure in turn persuaded a notable group of scientists to join in the experiment. These came down the Ohio in a boat called the *Philanthropist*, but which became widely known to newspaper readers of the day as the "Boatload of Knowledge."

However, in spite of its auspicious beginning, Owen's New Harmony colony functioned only a year or two before it passed out of existence. Its failure—along with that of virtually every other coöperative land experiment of the period—is said to have been primarily due to the fact that "there were too many managers and too few workers." However, unlike most such socialistic ventures, New Harmony continued to wield a potent influence in certain fields long after its original purpose had been abandoned. Of it, David Starr Jordan, who had followed its work closely while he was a professor and later president of the University of Indiana, wrote in 1927: "Its failure was in its economics; its successes in the field of nature. . . . But from another point of view . . . the episode must be reckoned a great success. It marked the advent in the Middle West of serious work in science."

In Dr. Jordan's view, credit for New Harmony's importance through the 1830's and 1840's and on down to Civil War times sprang partly from the work of the scientists assembled by William Maclure when the colony was first founded, and partly from the industry and talents of Robert Owen's three sons who had come out to New Harmony with him and who remained after the older man returned to England. All three presently attained eminence. David and Richard Owen became geologists of note, Richard as professor of natural science at the University of Indiana, and his brother David in a wider field. For, states Jordan, "The beginning of the United States Geological Survey was the work of David Dale Owen, and till near the time of the Civil War, its actual headquarters were at New Harmony."

The most widely known of this gifted trio, however, was the elder brother, Robert Dale Owen (1801–1877), who crowded into his seventy-six years an immense amount of work as author, politician, and social reformer, and who achieved distinction in all three fields. He was an industrious and able writer and his essays and novels and plays received wide popular acclaim during his lifetime. In politics he served one term in the Indiana legislature and two—from 1843 to 1847—in Congress. When he was a member of the House he was largely instrumental in securing passage of the act creating the Smithsonian Institution, a project that had been before Congress for a decade and that had engaged Owen's interest because of his close association with the scientific work being done at New Harmony. It was, however, in the sphere of social reform that he achieved his widest fame, his advocacy of liberal divorce laws and of woman's rights and his opposition to organized religion, among other equally advanced theories, winning him both warm supporters and bitter opponents and stirring up violent controversies in all parts of the land.

It was Robert Dale Owen's work in support of the Smithsonian legislation that brought him within the sphere of young George Davidson's interests. For Davidson's chief at the Coast Survey bureau, Superintendent Bache, had also been active in securing passage of the act, and Bache and Owen had thus become close friends.

Among the elder Robert Owen's children who had come with him from England to New Harmony was a daughter, Jane Dale Owen. In 1833, Jane, who has been described as "a woman of much ability and considerable scientific knowledge," was married to Robert H. Fauntleroy. It was, of course, this Fauntleroy-Owen union that resulted in bringing George Davidson into close contact with affairs at New Harmony. For Fauntleroy joined the Coast Survey in the mid-1840's, and Superintendent Bache put him in charge of a field party—of which young Davidson was a member—engaged in making surveys of the coastlines of Florida, Alabama, and other southern states. For the next several years this work was carried on each winter, and during parts of the following summers Fauntleroy and Davidson, who had become his chief assistant, retired to New Harmony, where they checked the results of the field work and prepared their charts and reports.

During these summers in Indiana young Davidson—he was still in his early twenties—was not only brought into close contact with the scientists and scholars gathered there but became well acquainted with the Fauntleroy family, including the four Fauntleroy children: two boys and two girls. Existing letters exchanged between the two men make clear that for a period of some three years they maintained a close friendship, which ended only when, early in 1850, the elder man fell victim to cholera while preparing to continue the Survey's work of charting the coast of Texas. He died at Galveston on January 13 of that year, being then in his forty-fourth year. Soon after his death, Fauntleroy's widow and their four children went to Europe, settling first in Stuttgart, Germany, and then in Italy, where her brother, Robert Dale Owen, throughout the early and middle 1850's, was United States minister to the Kingdom of Naples.

Davidson, who in the meantime had been sent to California, during the next few years conducted a voluminous long-distance correspondence with the Fauntleroys, regularly exchanging letters not only with Jane Dale Fauntleroy but with her two daughters, Constance and Ellinor. The letters of these teen-age girls, all of which Davidson carefully preserved, today possess a quaint charm: besides describing life on the continent a century ago as seen through the eyes of these two high-spirited adolescents, they express the girls' concern for the safety and well-being of their old family friend—Davidson was some ten years their senior— amid what they conceived to be the dangers and crudities of far-off California.

This exchange continued while the family remained abroad, a period of five or six years; and soon after their return to New Harmony, Davidson—who had temporarily returned to duty on the east coast—visited them there. Either then or later, Davidson and Ellinor, the younger of the two sisters, became engaged. They were married at the home of the bride's uncle at Whiteport, Virginia, on October 5, 1858.

Although the twenty-one-year-old bride, whom her husband called Ellie, was in uncertain health, having never fully recovered from an attack of fever she had had when abroad, the pair spent their honeymoon on a voyage to California via the Isthmus of Panama. Upon their arrival, Davidson promptly resumed his duties with the Survey; and thereafter she accompanied him on his field work whenever that was practicable, in spite of her physical frailty, willingly sharing the hardships of life in the primitive camps set up at observation stations on remote points on the coast.

Many years later, Davidson wrote that she had frequently accompanied him on his mountain work and on the expeditions to distant parts of the world which he later undertook for the purpose of making astronomical observations. Her life in the field began, indeed, only a few days after her first arrival in California early in 1859, when she spent several weeks in a tent at an observation station newly established on the crest of Mount Tamalpais in connection with triangulation work then in progress.

V · mapping the pacific shoreline

Curiously, Davidson's first impressions of the west coast—which was to be his home for more than sixty years and to the development of which he was to contribute much—were far from favorable. Soon after he arrived in 1850 he wrote to a friend in the East: "Combine all the worst features of New England, make every hill barren—no roads, no timber, no houses—and you will get a country in which no man will work while he can live elsewhere."

This opinion, by no means an uncommon one among those who in the early days came out from the populous and orderly communities of the Atlantic seaboard, undoubtedly sprang from his first contacts with a way of life markedly different from any he had previously known. For the California of the early 1850's was indeed a remote and unsettled land, the entire area, except for a few centers of frontier civilization, being wild and primitive in the extreme.

Moreover, the work on which he was engaged during the first years kept him almost continuously in regions far removed from all contacts with urban life. For months at a time he and his party were encamped on isolated coastal promontories or mountaintops while they made their surveys and observations, often at points that could be reached only from the sea, there being no roads or trails by which they might be approached from the land side. Also, as stated earlier, the landing of men and their supplies and equipment through the surf was a laborious and sometimes dangerous process; and presumably it was from his frequent immersion in cold water during the loading and unloading of the small boats, that the rheumatism developed which in later years was to cause him intermittent periods of acute pain.

But it was not long before his new surroundings came to seem less strange and unfriendly. For he was an active youth, physically strong and with a natural liking for the challenges and rewards of frontier life. Indeed, after five years on the coast, when he had begun to think of the likelihood of his being recalled permanently to the Survey's headquarters at Washington, his attitude had so changed that, in January, 1855, he wrote his future mother-in-law, Jane Fauntleroy: "How stupid it will seem ever again to sit quietly and cogitate before a fire . . . to grow gray headed and take a pew in church in order to appear respectable."

During these first years he was, in the words of one of his associates, "specially engaged in the definition of the latitude and longitude of prominent bays, capes, etc., and of the magnetic elements of the Pacific Coast, reporting also upon the proper locations of light-houses." That these duties, essential to the safety of the heavy water-borne commerce of the region, were satisfactorily performed is indicated by the fact that Superintendent Bache once stated that it was mainly because of the tangible results of Davidson's work there in 1850 and 1851 that succeeding Congresses approved further appropriations that made possible a continuance of the Survey's operations on the west coast.

A résumé of his activities throughout that period may be found in the annual reports of the bureau's superintendent. That for 1852, for instance, contains extended excerpts from Davidson's account of his party's observations and surveys of the preceding twelve months. Throughout that period, his group, working in close coöperation with Lieutenant Alden's hydrographic party, examined Trinidad and Humboldt bays and conducted extensive surveys of the mouth of the Columbia River. The result of their joint work was the publication by the Survey of charts not only of the entrance to the Columbia, but of San Diego, San Francisco, and Humboldt bays and of points Conception and Pinos.

The following year was equally productive. The little Survey schooner *Ewing* was discarded for a more efficient vessel, the ancient but seaworthy steamer *Active*. That this craft was accurately named is clear from the results of the year's work. This resulted in the publication, early in 1853, of a "Reconnaissance Chart of the Western Coast of the United States from San Francisco to San Diego," containing detailed charts of the principal harbors and anchorages between those two ports, including Monterey, San Simeon, San Luis Obispo, San Pedro, and the ports of the Channel Islands.

Most of 1853 was spent in carrying the survey northward from San Francisco; Alden, as before, mapped the shorelines of bays and inlets and promontories while Davidson set up stations ashore and by astronomical observations determined their exact positions. During the *Active*'s progress up the coast, surveys were made at Bodega Bay, Haven's Anchorage, Mendocino City,

Shelter Cove, and elsewhere on the rugged northern California shore. From there the party continued on to Port Saint George, Port Orford, and other points in Oregon and Washington territories, and finally to the Strait of Juan de Fuca, where they made an extended reconnaissance and prepared charts of Cape Flattery, Neah Bay, and Dungeness Harbor.

Much of Davidson's work in the next two years was in the North, centering in and about Puget Sound. In June, 1854, he was granted a ship for the use of his own party. He accordingly purchased in San Francisco a small but sturdy brig, which he renamed the *R. H. Fauntleroy* in memory of his admired friend and former officer of the Survey. Of the craft he wrote: "I hope she may prove as reliable and as serviceable to the Survey as he was." In one of his reports to Superintendent Bache for that year he stated that he had himself paid the cost of fitting out the vessel, his reason being that the government appropriation for that year had not yet become available, and he did not want his party to miss the period in the North when the weather was most favorable for observations. Months of work in the Puget Sound area followed: land stations were established at various points along the shoreline while observations were made to determine the exact positions of harbors, capes, and other prominent landmarks.

Davidson's findings for that year, and those of Lieutenant Alden's hydrographic party, resulted in the publication by the Survey of a chart entitled "Reconnaissance of the Western Coast of the United States from San Francisco to the Umpqua River," which did for the coast of northern California and much of Oregon what had been done southward to San Diego during the previous twelve months. The following year, 1855, this work was completed by the issuance of a third reconnaissance sheet extending the survey from the Umpqua River northward to the Canadian border.

In the meantime, surveys had been made and charts published

of a score or more harbors, inlets, and other anchorages along
some 1,500 miles of coastline, including Santa Barbara, Santa
Cruz, Drake's Bay, the Farallones, Crescent City, and many more
northern points. Fixing the exact geographical positions of these
had all been Davidson's responsibility. Another important phase
of his work was, as has been stated, to determine places where
lighthouses should be erected and to choose for their sites the
points where the lights would be of maximum value to vessels
plying coastal waters. The Survey's annual *Reports* for these
years make frequent reference to his recommendations, which
gave detailed information about the sites on the various capes
and promontories where the lighthouses should be placed so as
to be visible from the seaward side over the widest possible arc.

Some of the methods used in fixing the positions of important
coastal points are outlined in the Coast Survey *Report* for 1853,
in which Superintendent Bache wrote: "From October until
March last, Assistant George Davidson . . . was engaged in ob-
serving moon culminations for longitude near San Francisco.
During this time he also determined the latitude of Point
Reyes, . . . Sir Francis Drake's bay, by the zenith telescope, and
the approximate difference of longitude from San Francisco by
chronometer." That same active period found Davidson engaged
in triangulation work, fixing the location of the Channel Islands
in the south, and laying out base lines to be used in future surveys. Bache's report for 1853 continues: "A reconnaissance was
made in the autumn of last year, and this spring a base of about
six and three-tenths miles in length was carefully measured with
rods, near San Pedro . . . Mr. Davidson . . . proceeded with the
hydrographic party of Lieut. Comg. Alden to the coast of Oregon,
determining approximately astronomical positions, and making
sketches of the coast."

The *Report* for the following year, 1854, reveals that, during
the early months, Davidson and his party were occupied with
"a preliminary triangulation of the Straits of Rosario" in Wash-

ington Territory, and that later the group proceeded down the coast to Humboldt Bay and established a triangulation station there. In Bache's résumé of the year's activities is this comment: "Mr. Davidson has suffered very much during the past year with chronic rheumatism; persisting, however, in keeping [in] the field, that his work might be closed up at the end of the season, when he had received instructions to report on the Atlantic Coast."

In response to these orders, Davidson and his chief assistant, James S. Lawson, returned to Washington in the spring of 1855. However, both men, in spite of having spent nearly five years of strenuous field work in the West, signified a desire to return and carry forward the surveys and observations already well advanced. This wish was granted, and the summer of the following year, 1856, found Davidson once more in the Puget Sound area in the *R. H. Fauntleroy*, where, in connection with his triangulation work, he measured a base line at Port Townsend similar to the one he had laid out at San Pedro three years earlier.

It was while so engaged that he was able to pay a graceful compliment to his former associate, Robert H. Fauntleroy, in whose memory he had already named the ship under his command. During all his stay on the west coast he had, as mentioned earlier, kept up correspondence with Fauntleroy's widow and two daughters, who were then living in Europe. An important part of the Survey's work in connection with mapping the coastal area was the determining of the correct names of capes, bays, and other topographical features. In this phase of his duties Davidson from the beginning took a keen interest; it led him to familiarize himself with the voyages of the early explorers who had touched on the coast, and with the names they had given to its geographical features. Davidson's researches in that field begun at this time soon made him a recognized authority on the subject, and his interest in it continued as long as he lived.

His interest in place names had the full approval and encouragement of Superintendent Bache, who wrote that "it is of the greatest importance to trace the history of the discovery of the coast, to ascertain the original and successive names of places, and to go back to the earlier ones when the later ones have not become too permanently attached to the localities. . . . [Davidson's] aim was to make the Coast Survey maps and charts the standard for names and their spelling, as well as for the geography of the country."

In preparing his maps, however, Davidson found it necessary to confer names on some of the capes, mountains, inlets, and other landmarks that had not hitherto been christened, or the original names of which had either been lost or for one reason or another were deemed inappropriate. Thus he presently had an opportunity to do honor not only to the memory of his friend but to his correspondents in distant Germany and Italy. For while he was engaged in triangulation work in the Puget Sound area in 1856 it fell to his lot to name certain high, snow-covered peaks near the southeastern end of the Olympic Mountains. To these he gave the names of the four Fauntleroy children: the tallest, 7,777 feet high, he called Mount Constance; the next (6,500 feet) he named Mount Ellinor; and the third (6,920 feet) he christened The Brothers, for the two younger Fauntleroy children. These three lofty mountains, known collectively as the Fauntleroy Peaks, are clearly visible from Seattle. That city also has a Fauntleroy Cove—which presumably also was named by Davidson—and a Fauntleroy Park, not far from the cove.

VI · the limantour claim

Through much of 1857 Davidson was ill with persistent attacks of rheumatism, which from time to time became so severe as to necessitate his return to San Francisco for treatment. The sketchy diary he kept during that period makes frequent references to this; the entry for May 4, 1854, which reads: "Very unwell, took teaspoonful of laudanum," was typical of many others. Nonetheless, during the major part of 1857 he spent much time in the field, being then engaged in triangulation work in the area from the Sonoma County coast southward to Monterey.

By this time, moreover, after seven years on the coast, he had come to occupy an important place in the life of the area, particularly because of his participation in the scientific activities that were then getting under way. One of the first events to bring him to the attention of the generality of the citizens of San Francisco was his appearance as an expert witness in the sensational and long-drawn-out trial of José Y. Limantour. For the Limantour Case, as it came to be called, was one of the most important in the legal annals of the city, and the testimony Davidson—then a twenty-seven-year-old assistant on the Coast Survey—gave had a decisive bearing on its outcome.

Limantour was a Frenchman, long resident in Mexico, who in the mid-1850's had filed with the federal authorities what purported to be a number of land grants issued to him some ten years earlier by the Mexican governor of the province, Manuel Micheltorena. These apparently gave him title to four square leagues of land at the northern end of the San Francisco peninsula, together with the three largest islands in the bay—Angel, Yerba Buena, and Alcatraz—and the rocky Farallon group some twenty miles offshore. Limantour stated that title to this extensive area had been conferred on him by Micheltorena in return for a loan of $4,000; and in support of his claim he produced various documents, all carrying the official seal of the Mexican provincial government and seeming to bear out his contention.

When Limantour first made known his possession of these papers, San Franciscans were little concerned. Grants of land made by the Spanish and Mexican authorities before the conquest had quite generally been disregarded by the '49ers, who had settled where they liked, claiming title on the theory that the transfer of the province to the United States had invalidated the grants to former owners. However, one of the provisions of the Treaty of Guadalupe Hidalgo, by which California was ceded to the United States in 1848, specified that authentic titles to land issued by the former rulers would be considered valid; and a federal land commission had been sent out from Washington to carry out this complex task of passing upon such claims, which numbered in the hundreds.

It was not until the commission had examined Limantour's documents and pronounced them genuine that San Franciscans awoke to the seriousness of their situation. They had ample cause for alarm, for if the Frenchman's claims were substantiated by the courts, their own titles to property over a great area of the peninsula, including the entire central part of the city, would be invalidated.

The case came to trial in the fall of 1857 in the United States District Court, presided over by Judge Ogden S. Hoffman. So important were the issues involved that President Buchanan sent Attorney General Jeremiah S. Black from Washington to take personal charge of the forces opposing the claims. It was early recognized that the outcome hinged on the authenticity of the documents themselves, and much of the testimony pro and con centered about them, with Limantour and his attorneys stoutly maintaining that they were genuine, and the opposing side just as insistently pronouncing them forgeries.

It was on this all-important question that Davidson, on November 3, 1857, was called on to testify. The specific point on which his opinion was sought concerned the seals that Mexican officials of the province stamped on all official documents as a means of authenticating them. The seal employed at the time the Limantour grants were assertedly executed was that in use at the customhouse at Monterey. This was an adaptation of the coat of arms of the Republic of Mexico, consisting of an eagle clutching a serpent in its beak, over which were the words "Ad^a. Marit^a. De Mont^y." (*Aduana Maritima de Monterey;* that is, Maritime Customhouse of Monterey).

Davidson had earlier been asked to make a complete and detailed examination of the seals on six different documents. Three of these had been executed at Monterey in Micheltorena's term as governor, and their authenticity was acknowledged by both sides. The other three were those on which Limantour's claim rested. On the witness stand, Davidson, having been shown the six documents, testified that his scientific examination of their seals had disclosed that the first three had been stamped from the same original die, and that those on the three Limantour documents had been made with another, quite different, stamp.

Since to the eye of the casual observer all six seals appeared to be identical, this opinion created a sensation in the courtroom. The witness, however, after stating that his work with the Coast Survey, particularly in the field of triangulation, had made him proficient in the use of precision instruments and the measurement of minute distances, went on to point out a variety of discrepancies in the two sets of seals, all of which, while scarcely visible to the unaided eye, were quite apparent when examined under the microscope. Point by point, he went over enlarged reproductions of the seals, drawing attention to slight but unmistakable variations in, among other things, the curvature of the right wing of the eagle, the shape of the tail and tongue of the serpent, and the formation of several of the letters in the accompanying inscription. Davidson later stated that his conclusion that the seals were forgeries had been reached "after sixty hours of continuous work."

This testimony, which in spite of strenuous efforts the Limantour attorneys were unable to shake, marked a turning point in the long and bitter trial, for it strongly bolstered the prosecution's contention that the documents were fraudulent. On the day after his appearance in court, the *Daily Alta California* commented editorially: "The deposition of Mr. Davidson . . . demonstrates the subject in a very clear, and scientific manner. To every one reading this evidence, it must be clear that the Limantour seals are forgeries."

In any event, the case—which Attorney General Black pronounced "the most stupendous fraud, the greatest in atrocity and magnitude the world had ever seen"—soon collapsed, and its leading figure fled to Mexico to escape arrest and prosecution. Ironically, the wily Limantour carried with him a very substantial sum of money—some accounts place the amount as high as $200,000—which had been paid over to him by scores of San Francisco property owners in the weeks during which the trial was pending, in return for quitclaim deeds designed to clear their titles should his claim be upheld by the courts.

In the fall of 1857 Davidson was recalled to Washington, and there, during the next few months, he completed work on his first important publication. This, which bore the title "Directory for the Pacific Coast," was a comprehensive guide to navigation of the coast from San Diego to Puget Sound, a monumental work on which he had been intermittently engaged since 1853 and which was first published in the Coast Survey *Report* for 1858, where it occupied some 160 pages of closely set type.

Much of the time while he was preparing this work for the printer he lived with his mother and sisters and brother at Philadelphia. In May, 1858, he spent some weeks at New Harmony, Indiana, where, as stated earlier, his courtship of the younger Fauntleroy sister, Ellinor, resulted in their marriage on October 5. Soon after the wedding, the pair set out for California.

Davidson's next two years were busy ones, during much of which time he was, in his own words, "doing primary and secondary triangulation work north of San Francisco and astronomical observations in connection with it." In the summer of 1860 he was painfully injured by a fall while he was installing a signal on a mountaintop above Fort Ross, in Sonoma County, and he therefore returned to San Francisco to recuperate. However, he was back in the field a month later, and the work went on until, in September, word came recalling him to Washington.

In the meantime he and his wife had been saddened by the death of her younger brother, Edward H. Fauntleroy, a youth not yet twenty, who had joined the Survey and had been sent out to the coast as one of Davidson's assistants. And on November 18, 1859, Davidson's diary records the birth of their first child, a son, whom they named George after his father. (The diary entry for the next day reads: "Trotting around playing errand boy to the newcomer.") The boy died, as a result of a fall, in April, 1861, after his parents had returned East.

VII · civil war

Davidson and his wife and child sailed for New York on November 1, 1860, and nearly seven years passed before he returned to the west coast.

On reaching headquarters at Washington he took up the work of "recomputing all the observations of vertical angles made . . . in 1859 and 1860." In the meantime, however, the long-drawn-out controversy between the North and the South had been growing steadily in bitterness, a fact of which Davidson was, of course, well aware. Indeed, he later wrote that when he had left San Francisco for the East in the fall of 1860 it was "with the conviction that the conflict was soon to become a verity."

Davidson was at New Harmony when, the following April, the momentous news of the firing on Fort Sumter reached that quiet Indiana community. He returned at once to the home he had established near Philadelphia and offered his services in whatever capacity they might be needed. There he learned that Superintendent Bache—who was an engineering graduate of West Point—had been made a member of a committee charged with gathering geographical information for use by the Navy in its plans for establishing a blockade of the Confederate ports.

Davidson, having, as he stated, "served four seasons on the Southern coast," was called on to help in this work of the committee. Never completely content with a desk job, however useful or important it might be, on the completion of that assignment he asked for work in the field. He was accordingly delegated to make a survey of the Delaware River above Philadelphia and, when that was finished, to resurvey the lower reaches of the river. This was a task of considerable importance, for, as he later recalled, "Professor Bache had informed me that the Government had positive information that the old *Merrimac* was being prepared for an attack either upon Washington, Philadelphia, or New York, and that it was essential to know every feature of the channels in these two parts of the Delaware."

After these surveys had been completed, he received, in March, 1863, a telegram directing him to be ready for immediate duty "to make a special and detailed survey of Fort Delaware for defense." Further orders instructed him to prepare plans for blockading the Delaware at a point below Philadelphia and for destroying all buoys and other navigational aids in the river. While engaged in this he worked out a plan designed to checkmate the *Merrimac*'s expected raid on the city by sinking in the river's channel below that port a number of coal-carrying craft from a near-by suburb. Many years later, in writing of this he stated that "a very few of the loaded ones would have blocked the channels and could have been easily raised afterwards." It was, however, never necessary to put this carefully worked out program to the test, for, as Davidson adds, "the *Merrimac* never got inside Chesapeake Bay and the Delaware channels and buoys were undisturbed."

In that same period he was entrusted with another mission, one that involved work of a quite different sort. Word had reached the authorities that a woman living in Philadelphia had in her possession a chart giving information concerning the approaches to one of the Southern ports, which she had recently offered for sale in New York. Davidson was assigned to investigate the matter and, if the document had value, to secure possession of it or, failing that, to familiarize himself with its contents.

He succeeded in finding the woman and, by pretending to have Secessionist leanings, was able to persuade her to let him examine the paper. It proved to be a chart giving soundings and sailing directions for entering Wassaw Sound, one of the approaches to the city of Savannah. Recognizing its value, he entered into a long parley with the owner concerning its purchase price—she was asking $1,000 for it—all the while studying it closely so as to fix its details in his mind. Having done so, he left, stating that it would be necessary to get the approval of his superiors before the sale could be consummated. On returning home he redrew the document from memory and turned it over to the naval authorities.

Not until months later did he learn how the chart thus obtained was being used. Having been placed in charge of the Coast Survey steamer *Vixen* and sent on a surveying mission off the coast of Florida, on the voyage south he put in at Port Royal, South Carolina, and there met Admiral Samuel F. Dupont, who commanded the South Atlantic blockading squadron. "That was a capital copy you made of Mrs. B——'s entrance to Wassaw Sound," commented the Admiral. "Only one sounding was missing in the whole sketch; and we have never since let a vessel go in or out of Savannah by that route." The original chart was later obtained from its Philadelphia owner by government agents; it had been prepared by her husband, a Confederate sympathizer, who was then serving on a Union warship in Southern waters.

The Florida expedition in the *Vixen* started late in 1862. It was to be a part of certain naval and military operations there. The first of these was the contemplated capture of Fort Brooke on Tampa Bay, which would have put to an end the activities of a fleet of blockade runners plying between that port and Cuba. The function of the light-draft *Vixen* was to survey and chart the approaches to Tampa Bay so as to make it possible for the heavier warships to approach near enough to bombard the fort. In preparation for that hazardous assignment, the little vessel had been fitted out with guns in New York, and the ammunition had been stored in an improvised "magazine" below the wardroom. "My crew," wrote Davidson later, "was principally made up from the hospital in New York and my assistants were enthusiastic young colleagues of the Coast Survey."

On arriving at the scene, however, Davidson and his shipmates were disappointed to discover that the warships, not waiting for the *Vixen*'s preliminary reconnaissance, had made an assault on Tampa Bay and had been repulsed. "The commanding officer," he stated, "did not propose to renew the attack, although I begged to be allowed to survey the channel and buoy it out." Permission to do that, however, was not granted. The *Vixen*'s crew then spent some time in making a survey of near-by Indian Key, until instructions were received ordering the vessel back to New York.

Much of the next year, 1863, Davidson spent in laying out and building fortifications for the defense of Philadelphia. The greater part of this was emergency work done at a time when the city was believed to be in imminent danger of attack. For in mid-June of that year, Lee's forces, having crossed into Pennsylvania, were moving up the Shenandoah Valley; and advance troops of his cavalry were reported as being less than seventy-five miles from the city. From the standpoint of the Philadelphians, the situation was a highly dangerous one, for as Davidson wrote later, "had Lee known, there was not a company of soldiers at Baltimore, Philadelphia or New York, [and] he could have pushed part of his force to Philadelphia, where there were forty-two vessels under repair at the Navy Yard . . . destroyed the great arsenal at Bridesburg, and put the city under contribution for the amount of gold coins in the vaults of the banks."

In this same reminiscence Davidson recalled that news of the near approach of the Rebels thoroughly alarmed the residents, and plans were hastily improvised to repel the expected invasion. "At Germantown where I lived," he wrote, "church bells were tolled to draw the people together. For myself I started into the city with my rifle and 120 rounds to push on to the Valley."

However, on reporting to Bache, who was acting as chief engineer to General Dean, commanding in the area, he was given the assignment of laying out fortifications on the city's outskirts. "On the 27th of June," he reported, "I was placed in charge of the selection of sites for earthworks to prevent troops from entering by the great turnpikes along the left bank of the Schuylkill and parallel thereto."

To speed that work, other engineers were assigned by the railroads of the area, and by the city officials and technical schools, with the result that Davidson presently had the direction of a corps of more than thirty trained surveyors. Having selected the location for a nine-gun battery, and the site having been approved by Bache and General Dean, he was directed to proceed with the building of the battery with all possible speed. Work on it began on July 2, while the crucial Battle of Gettysburg was raging to the southwest; with sixty men and carts working night and day, it was completed and the guns were installed on July 4. However, the Confederate repulse at Gettysburg removed the immediate threat to the city, and the hastily thrown up battery, which was known as Fort Dana, was never put to the test.

Thereafter defense work continued, though at a less precipitate pace, and throughout the winter and spring Davidson was occupied with other similar projects. In all, some eighty square miles of the surrounding area was surveyed, and outer and inner lines of defense were laid out. In addition to preparing maps in connection with that work, Davidson wrote a detailed report covering some 200 pages, copies of which were filed with the city of Philadelphia, the War Department, and the Coast Survey. Under the strain of this active period, his health—always of uncertain quality at that stage of his career—broke down, and he was given no further assignments in the remaining months of the war.

Soon after the conflict ended, word reached him that his old friend and mentor, Alexander Bache, was seriously ill in England, where he had been sent on official business. At the urgent request of Mrs. Bache, Davidson sailed for London in May, 1865, spent some weeks traveling in England and Scotland with the invalid and his family, and in June accompanied him back to the United States.

During the following year, 1866, he was engaged on an important work undertaken by the Survey, one made possible by the laying of the first transatlantic cable, which had recently been put in operation. The purpose of this assignment was to determine with greater accuracy the longitude of points on the Atlantic Coast by means of a telegraphic exchange of time signals with the Greenwich Observatory in London, the official point from which longitude is reckoned. This experiment, which had been planned by Bache and British scientists during Bache's stay in England, required extensive preparations on this side of the Atlantic, including the stringing of telegraph wires in Maine and New Brunswick, a project which Davidson supervised.

VIII · alaska

After the completion of that complex series of longitudinal observations, Davidson was given another assignment, one that indicates the growing importance of the place he had come to occupy in the work of the Survey. The possibility of digging a canal across the Isthmus of Panama, which had been discussed since early Spanish colonial days, had in recent years become a lively public issue both in and out of Congress. This was particularly true immediately after the Mexican War and the annexation of the west coast territory in 1848.

Accordingly, in 1866, Congress authorized the sending of a
group of experts to the Isthmus of Darien to conduct a preliminary survey designed to determine the feasibility of a canal
at that point. Davidson was made a member of the expedition,
with the title of chief engineer. The party left New York on
January 1, 1867. Hardly had they reached Panama City, however, when he fell victim to one of the tropical fevers then preva-
lent in the area. He was critically ill for some time and unable
to take any active part in the survey. When he was again well
enough to travel, he was sent home to recuperate.

Soon after his return, his old chief, Alexander Bache, under
whom he had served since joining the Survey more than twenty
years earlier, died. Succeeding him as superintendent was Benjamin Peirce, a noted astronomer and mathematician, who had
been one of the founders of Harvard Observatory. Davidson's
interest in the work on the Pacific Coast, which he had helped
inaugurate, had remained keen throughout the seven years he
had been occupied in the East. Therefore, when, only a few weeks
after his return from Panama, his new chief proposed to send
him again to California, there to take charge of all the Survey's
work on the coast, excepting only hydrography, he accepted the
offer with pleasure.

However, before he took up his new duties, he was placed in
charge of what was in many respects the most important mission
that had yet been entrusted to him. For at that time negotiations
were in progress between Washington and St. Petersburg looking
toward the purchase by the United States of the vast, virtually
unknown territory on the northwest tip of the continent, then
known as Russian America, and opinion in this country was
sharply divided on the wisdom of expending some $7,200,000
of public funds for that purpose.

Many years later, in 1898, in a letter to Senator John T.
Morgan, Davidson outlined the circumstances under which he
had been drawn into the matter. "Public discussions," he wrote,

"soon developed the fact that the purchase was to be challenged in Congress, so after consultations of the Secretaries of State and Treasury [the Coast Survey then being a bureau of the Treasury Department] with Superintendent Peirce, the latter directed me to 'gather whatever information I could of the resources of that terra incognita.' " On being summoned to Washington in May, 1867, Davidson accepted the assignment even though it was, as he wrote, "against the judgment of my family and physician," because of his uncertain health. His selection for the post was, states Charles B. Davenport, "in consequence of his ability to make reconnaissance quickly and adequately."

Having undertaken the work, Davidson lost no time preparing to carry it out. He sailed from New York late in June, reached San Francisco on July 9, and after recruiting there a party of scientists who were to accompany him—including a botanist friend, Dr. Albert Kellogg, whom he signed on as the ship's physician—he headed north on the U. S. Revenue Cutter *Lincoln,* which had been assigned to his use. After stopping at Victoria, British Columbia, on July 27, the party two days later proceeded northward, following the inner channels between Vancouver Island and the mainland, and on August 3 reached Fort Simpson. There a stop of a week was made while the scientists conducted geological and botanical examinations and others in the party made surveys of anchorages in the vicinity.

Weather conditions, however, made astronomical observations impossible, and the expedition proceeded to Sitka, which was reached on August 11. The Russian capital, Davidson reported, was then a town of 116 houses, with a population of less than 1,000. He and his party were cordially received, both by officials of the Tsar's government and the local managers of the Hudson's Bay Company, which was the chief, and indeed almost the only, commercial and trading concern in the territory.

Davidson later observed that these two groups were most coöperative, willingly putting at his disposal such information as they had concerning the region's resources in minerals, fish, furs, and timber, as well as maps and other navigational data, weather observations, and so forth, but that the behavior of the group of Americans who had recently arrived in town was far less admirable. These, having made their way north on learning that the United States was about to purchase the territory, had preëmpted many of the most desirable locations in the town, he stated, and had refused to be dislodged, nothwithstanding the fact that the country was still under Russian rule since the sale had not yet been consummated.

After some ten days at Sitka, the *Lincoln* continued on to Kodiak Island and from there to Unalaska in the Aleutians, which it reached early in September. The party spent another week making observations and surveys there, and then, having completed its mission, turned southward. A second stop was made at Sitka, where further observations and surveys were made.

Because of the need for haste, and because of the unfavorable weather conditions that prevailed during nearly all their stay in Alaska, Davidson and his companions were beset by many difficulties in carrying out their objectives. These included, besides their geographical reconnaissance, arranging for the establishment of customhouse and revenue stations, making maps and soundings, selecting sites for lighthouses and other navigational aids, and surveying the commercial resources of the territory. Nonetheless, before turning southward, Davidson and his staff assembled a mass of material, in the collection of which he had, according to one commentator, not only drawn heavily on the Russian surveys and other records, but had "also made use of the knowledge of the principal Indian chiefs of Alaska."

On October 27 the return voyage began. Davidson and his associates must have been uncommonly busy, on the trip down the coast, for when the vessel docked at Victoria, he wrote Superintendent Peirce that he had assembled some 300 pages of reports and notes. On arriving at San Francisco the party disbanded, and its leader caught the first Panama steamer for the east coast. Before the end of the year he was back at his Germantown home putting the finishing touches on a 55-page preliminary report. He also journeyed to Washington and there gave an oral account of his findings to Secretaries Seward and McCulloch of the State and Treasury departments, and to Senator Sumner, chairman of the Senate Committee on Foreign Affairs, and also testified before the Finance committees of the Senate and the House.

On his return he found public interest in the purchase of Alaska keen throughout the nation, and for some time he was busy spreading abroad information about the little-known far-northern region. In the months that followed he delivered a number of lectures before audiences on both coasts and contributed the first of many magazine articles he was to write in the course of his career—a paper on the "Scientific Expedition to Alaska," which appeared in *Lippincott's Magazine* for November, 1869.

His full report—on which he was occupied during the early months of 1868, "working," he stated, "twelve hours a day"—was an extremely comprehensive document. It was published, as Appendix 18, in the Coast Survey *Report* for the year 1867, where it occupied some 140 pages of that bulky volume. It was said that the mass of detailed information he and his companions had gathered on their hurried survey, particularly concerning the resources of the territory, had much to do with overcoming opposition to the transaction both in and outside Congress and, in the words of one authority, "had great influence in the consummation of the purchase."

Davidson's interest in Alaska, first stirred by this 1867 visit, remained keen for many years. He visited the territory again two years later, this time on an astronomical mission, as head of a party dispatched to observe a total solar eclipse on April 7, 1869. His account of the results of the observation was printed as part of the Survey's *Report* for that year and was issued separately as a pamphlet. On this 1869 expedition Davidson penetrated far into the interior, proceeding up the Chilkoot River and thence to Fort Selkirk on the Yukon.

That journey, which he later stated had carried him into an area never before traversed by a white man, was attended by much hardship and considerable danger. He wrote that upon leaving Sitka he was "compelled to undertake the worst part of the journey in an open boat." This was a large war canoe, manned by four braves of the Sitka tribe. Besides Davidson and a single aide, it carried the astronomical instruments and a supply of provisions. Major General Davis, Commandant of the Department of Alaska, offered him an escort of soldiers; but this he declined, in spite of the fact that, as he wrote Superintendent Peirce, "The tribe of Chilkehts numbered 1500 and was considered the most hostile on the coast, especially as Davis had recently kept their chief ten days in the guardhouse and shot one or two of their men trying to pass the guard."

A further complication was that Davidson suffered a recurrence of Panama fever during the trip, which made him so ill that, as he informed his superintendent, "I had to be lifted into the boat sometimes . . . and in a country where the military officers considered me reckless in venturing with one aide and four men beyond the reach of military aid." Nonetheless, the party reached the designated point on schedule and set up their instruments in time to view the eclipse on April 7. Unluckily, however, weather conditions were unfavorable and prevented the making of altogether satisfactory observations.

Since Davidson had in 1867 been made head of the Survey's suboffice in San Francisco and placed in charge of triangulation and astronomical work on the entire Pacific Coast, Alaska after its purchase was included in the territory over which he had jurisdiction. Thereafter, as long as he remained with the Survey, he made persistent efforts to have Congress make appropriations that would permit badly need work to be done there. Congress, however, was for many years in a parsimonious mood as far as the northern possession was concerned and consistently refused to grant the appropriations he recommended. In 1898 he wrote: "I managed to keep the Coast Survey connection alive by the single thread of tidal observations at Kodiak Island until commerce demanded surveys of the channels through the Archipelago Alexander. Until that time the navigators depended on the work of Vancouver (1794) with additions by Tebenkoff (1848–52)."

In the meantime he had continued his effort to awaken public interest in the region by magazine articles descriptive of its resources and scenic attractions. Then, as the century ended, two events focused attention on the long-neglected possession: the discovery of gold in the Klondike in 1896 and, soon after, a controversy between the United States and England concerning the location of the boundary separating southern Alaska from British Columbia. In this Alaska boundary question, which for a time put a severe strain on diplomatic relations between the two nations, Davidson was deeply interested. Although his connection with the Coast and Geodetic Survey had terminated several years earlier, he had, drawing on his long and intimate knowledge of the region, prepared a lengthy treatise on the subject. This he made available to members of the American Commission—Elihu Root, Henry Cabot Lodge, and George Turner—who had been designated in 1903 to meet at London with three high British officials and arbitrate the matter.

That Davidson was long engaged in preparing that work is evidenced by a letter to a Philadelphia friend, Franklin Spender Edmonds, dated December 28, 1903, in which he wrote: "I have been very busy since April, when I undertook to draw up a paper on the Alaska Boundary Question." After stating that a copy had been put into the hands of members of the American delegation before they left New York, he added: "The Alaska Packers' Association [a group of San Franciscans extensively

engaged in fishing and other commercial operations in the north]
then started to have it printed, and after several unavoidable
delays it is now in proofs."

This 235-page work, dated 1903, contains, in addition to the
seventy-eight-year-old writer's reasoned analysis of the merits
of the boundary dispute, much of the early history of the area,
together with a discussion of its physical features and resources.
It contains, too, a highly interesting reminiscence of his first
visit to the territory in 1867, as well as a foreword in which the
publishers pay deserved tribute to the "comprehensive . . . scientific learning and indomitable energy" of the book's venerable
author.

IX · the coast pilot

In the fall of 1868 Davidson was back in
San Francisco, this time in charge of the Survey's work on the
Pacific Coast, a position he was to hold for more than a quarter
century. At his headquarters, which after 1874 were in the
big red-brick Appraisers' Building on Sansome Street between
Washington and Jackson, he planned the continuing survey and
charting of the extensive area under his jurisdiction. He was,
however, never long content to direct such operations from a
distance. As much of each year as he could spare from his administrative duties was spent in the field, usually on remote coastal
headlands or interior mountaintops where surveys or observations were under way.

Because his scientific interests were broad, embracing as they
did not only those in which he was primarily engaged but the
allied fields of astronomy, geology, anthropology, and a half
dozen others, it was not long until he became a recognized leader

in all such activities on the coast. Nor was he the type of scholar who pursued learning solely as an end in itself; his main interest was always the practical application of advances in science to the problems of commerce and industry. Thus, because his work for the Survey was in the first years primarily to promote the safety of navigation on the coast, he kept in close touch with the shipmasters whose vessels plied these waters, asking their frank opinions on the value of the charts and other aids supplied them and inviting suggestions for making these more useful.

Of this phase of his activities, his friend Alexander McAdie once wrote: "All the old navigators knew and trusted him implicitly. They brought him all records of strange happenings and went to him for advice. He made a special study of shipwrecks and helped more than any one man to make travel by water safe along the coast." In 1879 another acquaintance, in reviewing Davidson's contributions in that field, stated that he had "made his mark upon every foot of the extensive coastline from Panama to the Aleutians."

Because for nearly two decades after he had first begun his work on the coast, the transportation of both passengers and goods between California and the eastern seaboard was chiefly by means of vessels engaged in this trade—either via Panama or Nicaragua or round the Horn—he early recommended that the government conduct surveys not only of the coastlines of California, Oregon, and Washington but of those farther south. For it was in the section of their long voyages that lay between San Diego and Panama City that many of the disasters to American ships occurred, a goodly proportion of which he attributed to the fact that existing charts of that shoreline were few and far from accurate, and such useful aids to navigation as lighthouses and buoys were almost nonexistent.

Although Davidson had no success in this campaign—for Congress was reluctant to appropriate funds to be expended on foreign soil, and Mexico and the Central American countries had little interest in safeguarding the American ships plying their offshore waters—he continued, in his yearly reports, to urge Congress to take that action, relaxing his efforts only when, in 1869, the completion of the transcontinental railroad drastically reduced the volume of water-borne traffic between the two coasts.

Soon after he assumed charge of the Survey's suboffice in San Francisco, Davidson, as a means of fixing more accurately the longitude of points on the coast, had all triangulation positions from San Diego to Puget Sound connected by telegraph. In 1869 this work was extended by a series of telegraphic time signals between San Francisco and Cambridge, Massachusetts, by which, in Davidson's words, he "determined the signal time over 7200 miles of wire."

In the meantime he had begun a task that in the opinion of many was his most valuable single service to the cause of safe navigation in west coast waters. This work, which he did on a purely voluntary basis and at such times as he could spare from his official duties, he undertook because in his frequent travels up and down the coast he had accumulated a mass of information that he believed would be highly useful to all shipmasters whose vessels touched at the ports of the northwest coast. In that connection, he wrote on August 29, 1858, to Superintendent Bache: "For nearly eight years the duties to which you assigned me in California and in Oregon and Washington Territories, kept me moving continuously along the seaboard in every means of conveyance, and familiarized me with almost every mile of the coast . . . [these] along with my trips and explorations have amounted to an aggregate of between fifty and sixty thousand miles."

Observant by nature and ever aware that the Survey's primary purpose was to safeguard marine traffic in these waters, Davidson was at all times alert to matters bearing on this subject, making careful note of reefs, currents, weather conditions, and much else, until he presently had voluminous data relating to virtually every part of the coastline from San Diego to the Canadian border. He once stated that it was his habit, whenever the Survey ship in which he traveled from point to point approached close inshore, to carry a weighted line in his hand and take frequent soundings.

Much of the information thus gathered was, Davidson realized, known to nobody else, and in the mid-1850's he set about to find means of making it readily available to the masters of ships engaged in that commerce. Thus, in 1855, the annual *Report* of the Survey contained a 9-page appendix, "Extracts from a Descriptive Report . . . upon Localities . . . from the North Entrance of Rosario Strait, W.T., to the Southern Boundary of California," listing anchorages, navigational hazards, and other data gathered at numerous points along the shore.

However, as Davidson later stated, "the accumulation of observations on currents, winds, fogs, dangers, etc., warned me that I could not trust them to memory or desultory notes." Accordingly, in 1855, a part of the material was published in the *Alta California*, then a leading San Francisco journal, which was owned by Fred McCrellish, a close friend. Of this first publication of the information, Davidson wrote Bache that "although abounding in typographical errors, the avidity with which it was sought was a strong incentive to continue the self-imposed task." Thus encouraged, and because, as he added, he felt it his "duty that that knowledge should be put in proper shape and collated with the information and experience of others for the benefit of the growing commerce of the coast," on his return to the East later in 1858 he applied himself to putting the material in final form, working long hours daily for several months to complete the task.

The result, bearing the title "Directory for the Pacific Coast," appeared, as stated earlier, in the Coast Survey *Report* for 1858. Concerning its author's qualifications for the task, Superintendent Bache wrote: "Having thoroughly and peculiarly identified himself with the survey of the Western Coast from its beginning, and had occasion himself to know the necessities, facilities, and dangers of its navigation, he has been in a position to prepare a particularly valuable directory for the use of mariners and navigators."

Of the scope and purpose of the directory itself, Bache added:

The general plan ... is, to give a description of the bay, harbor, portion of the coast, its leading features, the history of its discovery, with notes of the previous maps and charts, and remarks of the earlier navigators, and a comparison, sometimes, of existing characteristics with those assigned in earlier times. The facilities for navigation, geographical position, and magnetic variation follow, with sailing directions for entering the bay or harbor, or passing along the coast. The leading features of the tides are given. General remarks close the paragraphs, each of which is headed with the name of the portion of the coast described in it. References are added, giving the dates of the Coast Survey charts for all the localities for which charts have been published.

It was indeed a comprehensive document, and although, as Davidson later recalled, the Survey undertook its publication "with some hesitation," it "received such practical endorsement from the navigators of the Pacific Coast that a second edition was called for in 1862 by Superintendent Bache and a third in 1869 by Superintendent Peirce." The usefulness of the work in its successive editions was so widely recognized among seafaring men of the coast that they dubbed it "Davidson's Bible"—a name of which its author declared himself proud.

As long as he remained with the Survey he continued assiduously to collect additional material bearing on the topographical and meteorological features of the area, as well as on its historical phases. When, in 1880, the then superintendent, Carlile P. Patterson, asked him to prepare a fourth edition, he found that, in his words, "the results of the systematic and extended surveys of my fellow workers on land and sea, the accumulation of a multitude of details where only general characteristics had before been available, the greatly increased number of aids to navigation ... and study through intervening years, could not simply be interpolated in the previous editions"; he therefore rewrote the entire work.

The fourth edition, published in 1889, like the third bore the title "Coast Pilot of California, Oregon, and Washington" and stands among Davidson's major writings in the field of Pacific Coast geography, history, and navigation. To the preparation of this ponderous 700-page work, he gave whatever time he could spare from his other duties, for a period of eight years. "Every line" of the last preceding edition had been rewritten, he wrote in 1890 to his sister in Philadelphia, the manuscript contained some 3,500 pages and, he added, no one had yet found in it any inaccuracies "beyond a few typographical errors."

The thick volume not only fulfilled its primary purpose of supplying mariners with detailed and authentic navigational information on every part of the coastline but went much beyond that by delving deeply into the historical phases of the subject, painstakingly tracing the routes followed by the earliest explorers, identifying their stopping places, and evaluating the accuracy of their observations and charts. The historical part of the work, in fact, made the volume, in the words of one authority, "the most comprehensive work ever published on that phase of the history of the coast, and ... an extremely valuable source of information to later writers on the subject." Of it, Rear Admiral Leo Otis Colbert, a later Director of the Coast and Geodetic Survey, wrote as recently as 1949: "This volume ... has become one of the great historical documents of the Survey"; and J. J. Gilbert, writing in the *Bulletin* of the American Geographical Society in January, 1912, stated that "its wealth of valuable historical and geographical information" was the result of the author's "remarkable capacity for study and research."

This monumental 1889 *Coast Pilot* was the last with which Davidson—who was in his sixty-fourth year at the time of its publication—had any direct connection. When continuing sur-

Alexander Dallas Bache, 1806–1867. Superintendent of the U. S. Coast Survey from 1843 to 1867

The first building of the Central High School, Philadelphia, 1838–1854

Headquarters of the California Academy of Sciences from the mid-1870's until 1891. This former home of the First Congregational Church was at the corner of California and Dupont streets San Francisco. Courtesy, Society of California Pioneers

The old Fauntleroy house, New Harmony, Indiana

An early view of Lick Observatory, Mount Hamilton, California. Courtesy, Society of California Pioneers

The Davidson Observatory, Lafayette Park, San Francisco. This first astronomical observatory on the Pacific Coast was built and equipped by Davidson in 1879 and was maintained by him for more than a quarter century

Davidson's wife, the former Ellinor Fauntleroy, and their two sons, George F. Davidson (left) and Thomas D. Davidson. From a photograph taken in San Francisco in 1869

The U. S. Coast Survey brig *Fauntleroy* at Port Townsend. This first Coast Survey ship on the West Coast was named by Davidson in memory of Robert H. Fauntleroy

Central Court of the California Academy of Sciences, 844 Market Street, San Francisco. A gift of James Lick, this building was occupied by the Academy from 1891 until it was destroyed in the fire of 1906. Courtesy, California Academy of Sciences

Scientists inspecting newly discovered prehistoric footprints at the Nevada State Prison, Carson City, 1883

Mount Davidson, Nagai Island, Aleutian Islands. Named for Davidson in 1871 by the naturalist William Healey Dall

Observatory on the summit of Mount Conness, California, August, 1890. Davidson standing at left

Coast Survey party in the field, summer of 1890. Left to right: Davidson, Gilbert, Winston, an unidentified man, and Edmonds

Mount Ellinor, Washington, from Lake Cushman. One of three peaks in the Olympic Range—Mount Ellinor, Mount Constance, and The Brothers—named by Davidson in the early 1850's for the children of Robert H. Fauntleroy

Easter sunrise services on Mount Davidson, San Francisco

Davidson Glacier, Chatham Strait, Alaska. Named for Davidson in 1867 by
Alexander Dallas Bache. The dark line in the foreground is a forest of tall pine
trees covering the terminal moraine

Fauntleroy Cove, Seattle, Washington. So named by Davidson in the early 1850's in memory of his friend and former fellow member of the Coast Survey staff

Davidson before his tent at a Coast Survey camp in January, 1889, when the Los Angeles base line was being measured

Officials of the U. S. Coast Survey. From a photograph taken in
Washington, D. C., in the early 1890's. Davidson is in the middle
of the front row; on his left is Thomas Corwin Mendenhall,
Superintendent of the bureau from 1889 to 1894

Professors George Davidson (left) and Joseph LeConte. Photograph taken in 1910 on the day Davidson received the honorary degree of LL.D. from the University of California

veys and the installation of new aids to navigation made necessary the periodical reissue of the *Coast Pilot,* the historical phases
of the old work were omitted and it became, and remains to this
day, a strictly utilitarian handbook for mariners whose ships ply
Pacific Coast waters.

Besides writing the four editions of the *Coast Pilot of California, Oregon, and Washington,* Davidson in 1869 produced
another important work in the same field: the *Coast Pilot of
Alaska* (First Part), *from Southern Boundary to Cook's Inlet.*
This 251-page volume, too, bears heavily on the historical phases
of the subject, the author stating in his introduction that "the
narratives of the old navigators, explorers, and fur-traders, have
been in great part examined and collated for special descriptions
of bays, harbors, straits, headlands, islands, coast line, currents,
fishing banks, &c." That Davidson went into this phase of the
subject with characteristic thoroughness is indicated by his state-
ment that: "Among the authorities examined have been Müller,
Coxe, Cooke, Meares, Portlock, Dixon, La Pérouse, Vancouver,
Lisianski, Kruzenstern, Kotzebue, Wrangell, Beechey, Seemann,
George Simpson, Thomas Simpson, Venjaminoff, Tebenkoff,
Holmberg, Grewingk, Annals of the Observatory at Sitka, together with many manuscript maps of the Russian-American
Company, and verbal communications from the navigators of the
company."

X
• earthquakes
and irrigation

With his all-inclusive interest in the phys-
ical sciences, Davidson was of course a close student of a natural
phenomenon that was not infrequent on the Pacific Coast—earthquakes. During his long residence in California he had ample

opportunity to study the subject; he once stated that in that period he had experienced some seventy-five earth movements of greater or lesser intensity. The first widely destructive visitation, however, was that of October, 1868, which caused widespread property damage in and about San Francisco, numerous injuries to persons, and some loss of life.

Davidson was one of a committee of three appointed by the city authorities to make a survey of the damage and to suggest ways of coping with such emergencies should they arise again. The committee's report recommended, among other things, that steps be promptly taken to construct reservoirs at strategic points throughout the city as a safeguard against the failure of the water supply should future earth movements break the mains and render the regular distribution system useless. This warning, however, went unheeded; no action was taken. The consequence was that after the violent temblor of April 18, 1906, no water was available to combat the numerous fires that sprang up in the partially wrecked buildings, and the entire center of the city was destroyed.

His work in 1868 was by no means the first manifestation of his interest in the subject. More than eleven years earlier, on April 28, 1857, he wrote to Superintendent Bache concerning a phase of his professional work that had long held a particular interest to him—the invention of scientific instruments helpful in carrying on the work of the Survey or improvements in the design of those then in use. In this letter he announced that he was at work on an instrument, "not yet matured in detail," designed to measure and record the up-and-down movements of the earth during a quake.

Whether or not this particular device was ever perfected and put into use must be left to conjecture, since no further reference to it has been found in his subsequent correspondence. It is known, however, that in later life he had a seismograph placed in his San Francisco home. Mary McAdie, the widow of his fellow-scientist Alexander McAdie, once told of Davidson's disappointment that for many months after the instrument had been installed no temblors occurred, and stated that when the long-awaited shock eventually came he hurried home, eager to study the record of its duration and intensity. On his arrival, however, he discovered, to his disgust, that the movement had gone unrecorded, the reason being that a day or two previously he had removed the pencil from the instrument in order to sign a receipt for a delivery boy and had forgotten to replace it.

The highly destructive earthquake of April 18, 1906, naturally engaged a major share of his interest in the ensuing months. The fire that followed the quake left many families homeless. He at once turned over the astronomical observatory he had established in Lafayette Square as a shelter for the refugees. A week after the quake, on April 25, he thus wrote to a friend in the East of the effects of the catastrophe and the morale of the survivors: "There was no epidemic; there was capital order, with the military in charge; and those who remained are stout-hearted; the 125,000 encamped in parks, etc., are being fed. . . ."

Gertrude Atherton, the California novelist, later recalled having visited the scientist, a few days after the quake and fire, at his house on Washington Street, a few blocks beyond the outer rim of the burned area. "He was," she wrote, "alone and very willing to talk, but the only two remarks I remember were: 'My watch literally leaped across the room,' and 'Seismologically it was a number nine quake (number ten being complete devastation), but I think A-1 would be a better name for it!' "

A few weeks later, Governor Pardee appointed Davidson to a three-man commission charged with making a survey of the scientific aspects of the temblor; and in the following August, when the Seismological Society of the Pacific was founded, he became its first president. He continued to hold that office for three years and then his failing health forced him to resign. In the weeks following the disaster he wrote a detailed analysis of its scientific aspects, which appeared, under the title "Points of Interest Involved in the San Francisco Earthquake," in Volume XLV (pages 178–182) of the *Proceedings* of the American Philosophical Society, at Philadelphia.

From the time of his return to California in 1867, Davidson was frequently called on to undertake other assignments for which he was qualified by his wide knowledge of scientific procedures. In 1871 the Secretary of the Treasury delegated him to make an examination of the weights and balances in use at the U. S. Mint in San Francisco and to report on their accuracy. The following year, as a member of the U. S. Assay Commission, he made a similar examination of coinage at the Philadelphia Mint, during which, as he later wrote, he "personally made all the weighings and introduced new methods."

Late in the year 1872 he was engaged in surveying the section of the boundary separating California and Nevada that lies between the Oregon line and Lake Tahoe. While so occupied he made, from a peak in the High Sierra, a series of astronomical observations, in order, as he stated, "to test their relative value as compared with observations at small heights." It was as a result of these experiments that he advanced the then novel opinion that astronomical observatories would be more efficient if they were located at high altitudes. Two years later this theory was to have an important bearing on the founding of the famous Lick Observatory and the choice of a site for it, an enterprise in which Davidson was to play a decisive role.

Throughout the early 1870's, California's rapidly expanding agriculture having supplanted mining and stock raising as the state's sustaining industry, numerous projects were launched designed to increase the productivity of the land by means of irrigation. This was particularly true in the interior valleys of the Sacramento and the San Joaquin, over much of which the soil was extremely fertile and needed only sufficient moisture to yield prodigious crops.

For some years Californians had periodically been making representations to Washington urging the need for federal aid in carrying out these works, and early in 1873 Congress had responded by passing a bill creating a board of commissioners to investigate the matter and formulate plans for the development of methods applicable to conditions prevailing in the state's arid interior valleys. President Grant signed the bill in March of that year and named Davidson one of the commissioners charged with carrying out its provisions, the other two being Lieutenant Colonel B. S. Alexander and Major George H. Mendell, both officers of the Corps of Engineers, United States Army.

During the remainder of 1873 the three men made a thorough survey of water conditions throughout the area and studied its topography, climate, and other features. Their findings and recommendations were embodied in a 91-page paper with six maps, entitled "Report of the Board of Commissioners on the Irrigation of the San Joaquin, Tulare, and Sacramento Valleys of the State of California" (43d Cong., 1st sess., H. Ex. Doc. 290), which was published in 1874.

This work, however, did not exhaust Davidson's interest in the matter. In August, 1874, before sailing for Japan, where he was to head an astronomical party to observe a transit of Venus at Nagasaki, he received instructions to proceed round the world and, in his own words, "examine the condition and character of the irrigation and reclamation works of China, India, Egypt, Italy, etc., and report thereon."

Having become a recognized authority on irrigation and reclamation projects in foreign lands, Davidson, on his return to his post in San Francisco on March 6, 1876, read a series of papers on various aspects of the subject before the California Academy of Sciences, and between April 7, 1876, and February 14 of the next year, he contributed eight comprehensive articles on that then much-discussed topic to the San Francisco *Evening Bulletin*. Finally, by resolution of both houses of the California legislature, he delivered two addresses before joint meetings of these bodies, on February 17 and 18, 1877, on the subject "Irrigation in India, Egypt, Italy, and California."

Thereafter, for more than two decades, Davidson was frequently called on to make surveys and prepare reports on privately financed irrigation developments in the Sacramento and San Joaquin valleys. His published writings therefore include a number of pamphlets embodying his findings and recommendations in connection with such projects. These include a *Report upon a Scheme of Irrigation for the Waters of the Merced River* in 1877 (9 pages), a *Report upon the Engineering and Topographical Features of the Stanislaus and San Joaquin Water Company* in 1895 (46 pages), and a *Report of Board of Consulting Engineers . . . to the Landowners of Reclamation District No. 108* [*Sacramento Valley*] in 1896 (48 pages).

XI . the california academy of sciences

When Davidson and his three young assistants first landed at San Francisco in the summer of 1850, they found themselves in a confused and turbulent town that was undergoing the painful process of evolution from raw frontier camp to sedate, law-abiding community. For the town was then a cluster of canvas and rough-board stores and bars and hotels, interspersed with a few brick buildings, all fronting on narrow, deeply rutted streets that in the rainy season became bottomless quagmires of mud. Davidson's first impressions of the future metropolis were, understandably, not altogether favorable. In fact, during the early part of his stay, as previously mentioned, he could find little that merited praise, not alone in San Francisco but in all of California.

As time passed, however, his feelings, like those of many other recent arrivals from more settled communities, underwent a gradual change. Thus, some ten years later, on June 4, 1860, when he was about to be recalled to Washington, he wrote to his friend and confidant, Alexander Bache, that "I have a strong desire to make my home on the Pacific, notwithstanding many drawbacks"—adding cautiously, however, that "I shall not make up my mind until after my return to the Atlantic."

This change in his attitude toward the west coast was due to several factors, and though he at first pronounced the region thoroughly uncongenial, we find him a few years later seriously debating the possibility of making his permanent home there. Among the circumstances influencing that decision is almost certainly the fact that San Francisco and, to a degree, the state as a whole had in the years since his arrival made notable progress in casting off the crudities of the isolated frontier and adopting the conveniences and other marks of civilization that were sorely missed by those who had lived in the cultural centers of the East.

Clearly, Davidson was one of that group. Although throughout his life he thoroughly enjoyed periods of roughing it in the field, he was, both by training and inclination, a man of science, and there can be little doubt that during the early part of his stay he found the widespread lack of interest in scientific matters a prime source of discontent.

However, the decade of the 1850's had not far advanced before certain groups of pioneers, for the most part men who had been trained in one or another of the professions, set about laying the groundwork and providing facilities for organized study and discussion in the field of their interests. One of the earliest and most important of these was the California Academy of Natural Sciences, which came into existence in the spring of 1853. The original sponsors of the organization were seven men, five of whom were doctors of medicine. Its first public announcement stated that California represented "a virgin field with new characteristics and attributes, which have not been subjected to critical scientific examination," and concluded with this well-rounded sentence: "It is due to science, it is due to California, to her sister states, and to the scientific world, that early means be adopted for a thorough survey of every portion of the State and the collection of a cabinet of her rare and rich productions."

The early history of the Academy was fully as eventful—and as turbulent—as that of the city itself. Throughout the first three or four years, meetings were held in the Clay Street office of one of the founders, Thomas J. Nevins, San Francisco's first superintendent of schools. There the promised cabinet of specimens was duly installed, and there, too, the beginnings of a scientific library were assembled.

But although the Academy thus gained the distinction of founding the first museum and scientific library in the West, neither it nor its members wholly escaped the violence of the times. For in July, 1856, its first president, Dr. Andrew Randall, was shot down by one Joseph Hetherington, a member of a band of desperadoes then terrorizing the city, and the following day his assailant was brought before San Francisco's Second Vigilance Committee and sentenced to be executed for his crime. It is, however, a tribute to the Academy's single-minded devotion to science that on the evening of the day Hetherington was hanged in Portsmouth Plaza, its members met in their near-by Clay Street rooms for the purpose of examining and discussing two recent additions to its library: Michaux and Nuttall's *North American Sylva* and a pamphlet (title unrecorded) describing "new coniferous trees of California."

At what date Davidson's connection with the Academy began is not precisely known, but with his long-standing interest in virtually every phase of science it was inevitable that he would sooner or later become allied with the group. In any event, his name appears among the list of members in 1869. That from then on he took a leading part in its activities is indicated by the fact that two years later he was elected its president, a post that he was to hold continuously until 1887.

In the sixteen years he occupied that office the Academy made notable strides, rising from comparative obscurity to a position where it was recognized as one of the leading scientific bodies on the coast. That Davidson himself played a decisive part in this transformation is clear from the testimony of his associates, one of whom, Edward Bosqui, wrote years later that "no member of the Academy deserves more gratitude as an unselfish worker in [its] interests," and added that "he was in a position to do more for its ... permanent success than any other man."

A memorial printed in the *Proceedings* of the Academy after Davidson's death in 1911 pays a like tribute to the importance of his services, referring to him as "This distinguished member, and we might say founder, of the California Academy of Sciences," and stating that its existence "is largely owing to the work [he] did during its early history."

When Davidson took office in 1871 the Academy was, as he later wrote, "occupying two or three wretched rooms on Clay Street," evidently the same that had been its headquarters since the early 1850's. On September 2, 1872, the noted naturalist Louis Agassiz, in addressing members and their guests, made reference to their inadequate quarters in these words: "You have not rooms in which to display your acquisitions; you have not the means of making your pursuits inviting to the community at large; and with whom does it rest to foster these interests of intellectual growth? With those who have the means." Agassiz went on to call on the city's wealthy men to support the work of the Academy and thus permit California to "keep up the spirit which leads forward to intellectual growth," without which "there is no greatness for a State."

Whether or not Davidson, who presided at the meeting, drew

his inspiration from Agassiz's words, the fact remains that soon thereafter vigorous steps were taken to put the Academy on a sound financial footing and to provide quarters in keeping with its standing as the pioneer scientific body on the coast. Two years later, in 1874, a group of wealthy residents, including David Colton, Leland Stanford, and Charles Crocker, came to the Academy's aid by providing funds that enabled it to move out of its cluttered rooms into quarters commodious enough to permit the display of the substantial collection of specimens of the region's flora, fauna, and minerals it then possessed.

The building leased for this purpose was a church at the southwest corner of California Street and Dupont (now Grant Avenue), which had formerly been the home of the First Congregational Church, the church having recently vacated the premises on the completion of a new and larger structure at Post and Mason streets. There the Academy remained until 1891—a period of seventeen years.

Long before its next move, however, and mainly by Davidson's influence, the Academy had a financial windfall of a size that not only assured its permanence but made possible a great extension of its activities. Its benefactor was James Lick, the San Francisco capitalist. Lick, reputedly the largest owner of real estate in the city's downtown area, in 1874 deeded to the Academy a valuable piece of property on the south side of Market Street between Fourth and Fifth streets as a site for a new and permanent home. Davidson, who later wrote that the capitalist had "astonished us all by his unexpected gift," announced the news at the Academy's annual meeting in January of that year, terming it "a princely bequest" and adding that their unexpected benefactor "proposes to pay for the erection of new buildings for the Academy."

Upon the elderly philanthropist's death several years later, his will disclosed further munificence. Some $2,000,000 was bequeathed to the city and state for the erection of an astronomical observatory, the founding of a school of mechanical arts, and a variety of other purposes, including the establishment of public baths and purchase of statuary; substantial sums of money were also left for San Francisco orphan asylums, old ladies' homes, and similar charitable institutions. Moreover, the capitalist's will provided that after these specific bequests had been paid, the residue of the estate was to be divided equally between the Society of California Pioneers and the California Academy of Sciences. The result was that eventually each of these organizations received cash and property valued at approximately $600,000.

The result of Lick's generosity was that the Academy was able, in the late 1880's, to begin the construction of spacious new quarters on its lot at 833 Market Street. When this commodious brick-and-stone building was finished, in 1891, it contained stores and offices on the Market Street frontage, which yielded a substantial income from rents; ample museum and office space grouped about an inner court; and a spacious auditorium for lectures and other public meetings, which occupied most of the basement.

Here the Academy remained for some fifteen years. Its museum of natural history was one of the city's major attractions; not only was it visited by many thousands of local residents each year, but it became a mecca for visiting scientists. During all that time the exhibits were constantly being added to and their quality improved. Even before the funds for the new building had become available, one notable addition had been made to the Academy's collection. For in 1882, some ten years after Davidson had become president, a highly important traveling exhibit of scientific specimens was put on display at the Mechanics' Institute, and members of the Academy promptly launched a campaign to purchase it.

Davidson appointed a committee to look into possible means of raising the necessary funds—the price asked was $16,000— and the committee, with rare good judgment, invited Charles Crocker and Leland Stanford, the two railroad magnates, to attend its first meeting. The outcome of that move was all the committee could have hoped. For Crocker, on learning of the scientific importance of the specimens and the desirability of keeping them permanently in the city, volunteered to pay half the cost if Stanford would contribute the balance. The result was that each man wrote a check for $8,000, and the specimens were added to the Academy's growing collections. A third of a century later, however, all these, together with the organization's valuable library and many thousands of other specimens—including the locally famous re-creation of a huge mammoth and other prehistoric beasts in the central court—were destroyed in the earthquake and fire of 1906.

Long before that catastrophe, however, Davidson's connection with the Academy had drawn to a close. As stated, he had occupied the presidency continuously since his first election in 1871, during which time the organization had made notable strides. But at the annual meeting of members in 1887, when he was a candidate for that office for the seventeenth time, serious opposition to his policies developed, and when the ballots were counted it was found that he had been defeated, the vote standing at 80 to 102.

The precise cause of the contention which at that time divided the Academy's members into opposing camps is not definitely known. Miss Alice Eastwood, who was for many years the organization's botanical expert, once stated that a quarrel had developed over the use to which the Market Street lot given by Lick should be put, one faction maintaining that the museum ought to be located there, and the other that an income-producing office building should be erected on the site and the Academy's offices, library, and exhibition halls should be built elsewhere. However, the well-known San Francisco printer Edward Bosqui, long a director of the Academy and a warm friend of Davidson's, maintained that Davidson's defeat and his subsequent resignation were due to personal differences with Dr. H. W. Harkness, a local physician, who succeeded him as president. That Dr. Harkness was not the easiest man in the world to get along with is indicated by this story related by Bosqui. At one of the directors' meetings soon after Harkness became president, he got into an argument with Dr. H. H. Behr, a fellow physician who had been for many years an Academy director and on his retirement from practice had become its curator. Finding himself at a disadvantage in his verbal exchange with Behr, Harkness shouted: "Oh, go to hell!" To which the suave Behr answered politely: "After you, my dear sir."

Whatever brought it about, the quarrel that ended Davidson's active participation in the affairs of the Academy was unfortunate both for himself and for the institution he had headed so long and so successfully. For, as has been mentioned, during his term as president the organization had made substantial progress. Nor had this been accomplished without a great deal of well-directed effort on the part of the men in charge, and in particular of Davidson himself. For not only did the Academy, because of its president's standing in scientific circles, enjoy a greater degree of prestige than formerly, but it was for the first time put on a sound financial footing, chiefly as a result of his efforts to interest a group of the city's wealthy men in its activities.

However, Davidson's services were by no means confined to such matters. Throughout his entire adult life his major interest was in the field of science, and he never lost sight of the fact that the primary purpose of the Academy was to collect, preserve, and study materials bearing on its chosen subjects, to increase the sum of knowledge through research, and to foster an interest in these matters on the part of the lay public. In order to accomplish the last-named objective, the first step had been the establishment of a museum of natural history in the Academy's converted church on California and Dupont streets, which was open to the public at stated hours daily. A second step was the holding of frequent lectures on topics within the Academy's sphere, to which again not only members but the public were invited.

The files of the *Proceedings* of the Academy for the years when Davidson served as president indicate that he was uncommonly resourceful in securing qualified speakers at such meetings. If an eminent scholar in any field of science chanced to pass through the city, he was almost invariably prevailed on to address the members and their friends; and when such visitors were lacking, local men of science were pressed into service.

In the 1870's and early 1880's, however, the number of available speakers in either category was severely limited, and the consequence was that the president frequently stepped into the breach and himself addressed the meetings. Hence, the Academy's *Proceedings* for the period from 1872 to 1887 contain, besides a long series of annual President's Addresses dealing with the society's activities during the preceding twelve months, the texts of literally scores of other talks by Davidson. The following listing of a few of their titles will perhaps indicate not only his industry but the breadth of his scientific interests and the variety of subjects on which he had informed himself.

Thus, within a year or two after he became president, he addressed members on such topics as "The Effect of Temperature on the Sandstone Bluff near Buenaventura, Santa Barbara Channel," "The Relative Value of Great and Small Altitudes for Astronomical Observations," and "On an Improved Telemeter for Reconnaissance, Engineering, and Military Purposes." These, however, by no means exhausted his repertory, for in 1872 and 1873 he held forth on earthquake waves on the Pacific Coast, "The Probable Periodicity of Rainfall," and "On the Auriferous Gravel Deposits of California," as well as on the boomerangs used by the California Indians, "Mesh-Knot of the Tchin-cha-au Indians, Port Simpson, British Columbia," and "The Abrasions of the Continental Shores of N.W. America, and the Supposed Ancient Sea Levels."

Nor did the number or variety of such dissertations notably diminish during his remaining years in office. In the late 1870's and early 1880's he spoke on "The Transit of Venus," on the great comet observed in September, 1882, from Mount Tamalpais, and on "The Necessity for a Physical Survey of California"; and in 1885 he spoke on "The Temperature of the Water of the Golden Gate" and "Black Transits of Jupiter's Satellites III and IV."

After the Academy's Market Street building and virtually all its contents were destroyed in the 1906 fire, handsome new quarters were erected in San Francisco's Golden Gate Park. There the Academy has remained ever since, while over the years an impressive group of other buildings—the Steinhart Aquarium, the Simpson African Hall, and, most recently, the Alexander F. Morrison Planetarium—have sprung up about the original structure. Today the California Academy of Sciences is recognized to be, in the variety and quality of its exhibits and services, and in the beauty of its buildings and setting, one of the leading institutions of its kind in the country. When, in the spring of 1953, the Academy celebrated the hundredth anniversary of its founding, tribute was paid to the memory of those who had guided it through its difficult formative years, and on that list of pioneers the name of George Davidson deservedly stood high.

XII · the observatory in lafayette square

The mid-1870's was a particularly busy and fruitful period of Davidson's life. Toward the end of 1874 he, as has already been stated, headed an expedition to Japan to observe and photograph a transit of Venus. Headquarters were set up at Nagasaki, and the observations were conducted from a hilltop adjacent to the city. The result of his findings, which were carried out in the face of unfavorable weather conditions, was published in the Coast Survey *Report* for 1875, together with a series of photographs of the phenomenon. While in Japan he also, in his own words, "determined the telegraphic difference of longitude between Nagasaki and Vladivostok and Tokio," a service he had voluntarily undertaken and the costs of which he personally paid.

When this assignment had been completed, he continued on a journey round the world, in the course of which, in his capacity as a member of President Grant's Commission on Irrigation in California, he inspected irrigation and reclamation projects in China, India, Egypt, and Italy, and examined breakwaters, harbor and river improvements, and similar works in all the countries visited.

During nearly all the year 1875 he was engaged on this mission, sailing from Japan to Shanghai on January 27 and not returning to the United States until mid-November. His movements, briefly recorded in his diary, show that he reached Shanghai on February 4; Hong Kong on the eighth; Canton on the fourteenth; Singapore on the twenty-fourth; Calcutta on March 8; Arrah on March 14; and Bombay on April 11. In all, the indefatigable traveler covered 3,800 miles in India, visiting the principal regions under irrigation, consulting with engineers and high government officials, and gathering much information on the methods of water control and distribution employed there.

In early May he continued on to Egypt, and en route celebrated his fiftieth birthday, on May 9, at Port Said. Much of the remainder of that month he spent studying the methods by which the waters of the Nile were kept in bounds and distributed to the farming areas along its banks. He then crossed to Italy and for the next three months moved rapidly over the face of Europe, visiting in turn Naples, Rome, Florence, Venice, Munich,

Dresden, Berlin, Copenhagen, Amsterdam, and Frankfort. While on this hurried tour he somehow found time to visit the shops of the leading scientific instrument manufacturers in Paris, London, and Edinburgh, and was thus able to familiarize himself with recent advances in that field.

Davidson and his wife, who had accompanied him on his protracted tour, spent the winter of 1875–76 at Philadelphia, while he worked up the voluminous notes he had gathered on his travels. The result, entitled "Report upon the Methods Employed in Irrigating Land in India, Egypt, Italy, and Other Countries" was published in 1875. Another published result of his nine months of travel and observation in foreign lands was a paper called "Observations on Certain Harbor and River Improvements Collected on a Voyage from Hong-Kong, via Suez, to New York." This, like his report on his astronomical observations at Nagasaki, appeared as an appendix to the Coast Survey *Report* for 1875, and was also issued as a separate 24-page pamphlet.

Nor were these the only matters that engaged his attention during his world tour. While in India he, as he later wrote, "visited the field and conferred with the officers of the Great Trigonometrical Survey" of that country; when in Europe he likewise "visited the headquarters and officers of geodetic work in France, Prussia, Great Britain, and Switzerland." Moreover, in his capacity as a member of the Advisory Board of Harbor Commissioners of San Francisco—to which post he had been appointed two years earlier—he "examined the sewerage systems of Calcutta and the large cities of Europe." Finally, his keen interest in all scientific and engineering advances of his day led him to make a study of the mountain railroads of India and Europe and to write a paper comparing the problems involved in their construction with "those through the Rocky Mountains, Sierra Nevada and Cascade Mountains of the United States and Mexico." In view of all this, it is clear that Davidson's trip round the world was decidedly no mere pleasure jaunt.

By then more than a quarter century had passed since he had first taken part in the Survey's pioneer work of charting the west coast shoreline, and in that period he had come to occupy a position of leadership in many fields of scientific activity. Thus, by the time he was fifty, he not only was recognized as the West's most eminent man in his chosen profession, but since he had taken a very active part in many related phases of scientific research, he was looked on as a leading authority in these other fields as well. For from the beginning Davidson's professional interests had never been confined within the limits of his official duties; he was, in his own words, ever at pains to "keep abreast with all scientific progress correlated with the work of the Survey."

One of his major interests—which was, of course, closely allied with the Survey's work of determining the positions of capes, bays, islands, and other prominent coastal landmarks— was astronomy. His first acquaintance with that science had, as stated, begun in the early 1840's when, while he was attending the Central High School in Philadelphia, Professor Bache had made him a student observer, first at that school's observatory and then at Girard College.

Later, after joining the Survey, he had, of course, made many observations in connection with his work, both in the South and in New England, and, after 1850, on the Pacific Coast. Later still, after assuming charge of the San Francisco suboffice, he, as one of the most widely experienced astronomers on the Survey's staff, headed a number of parties assigned to observe eclipses and other celestial phenomena in various parts of the world.

Two of these expeditions have been briefly mentioned: those to Alaska in 1869 and to Japan five years later. A number of other such observations were conducted closer to home: from the top of Mount Tamalpais, from peaks in the Santa Lucia Mountains and in the High Sierra, and, in 1882, from the crest of the Cerro Roblero in New Mexico. These assignments all required extensive preparations and frequently involved severe hardships. For it was ever Davidson's theory that such observations could best be conducted at high altitudes, and accordingly at each location he chose to set up his station on the summit of the loftiest peak in the vicinity.

These mountaintops, of course, rarely had roads or trails of any sort leading up to them. Hence, the task of transporting equipment and supplies to the sites, and of building there the shelters in which the instruments were housed, required days and sometimes weeks of strenuous effort on the part of every member of the party. Moreover, some of these operations had to be carried out in midwinter—for example, the observations of the total solar eclipse made from the Santa Lucia Mountains in 1880—when, in addition to the obstacles presented by the rough terrain, the group had to contend with snow, sleet, and violent winds.

Among the most unusual and interesting of the astronomical observations Davidson conducted were those made in the spring of 1873 at the town of San José del Cabo on the peninsula of Lower California. This was for the purpose of locating the site from which Chappe d'Auteroche had observed a transit of Venus in 1769, and of checking the accuracy of the French astronomer's findings. The Coast Survey *Report* for 1874, in commenting on why this mission was undertaken, states: "It is believed that Chappe's observations are valuable; but they could not be fully utilized for want of a reliable longitude." It was to make them of greater use to scientists that Superintendent Peirce had authorized a reconnaissance of the spot by a party in the Survey steamer *Hassler* and had delegated Davidson to make the observations.

The record book Davidson kept during the expedition quotes from the diary of the French scientist, written more than a century earlier: "May 20, 1769.—I made haste to establish myself

at San José ... Myself and all my party took up their abode in
a large granary. I had half the roof taken off toward the south,
and put up an awning that could be spread out or furled at
pleasure. All my instruments were fixed just as they were to
stand to observe the transit of Venus. ... At last came the 3rd of
June, and I had an opportunity of making a most complete
observation. ..."

In his record book Davidson goes on to describe the steps by
which he located the precise spot where Chappe's instruments
had been placed. The task was complicated by the fact that the
church which had stood in the village in the earlier day had long
since disappeared and had been replaced by a new structure.
Moreover, the priest then in charge there was an Indian who, in
Davidson's words, "knows nothing of dates." However, the priest
was able to point out some remaining fragments of the founda-
tions of the original church, and the spot where the vanished
granary "was traditionally reported to have stood." This information, Davidson wrote, and "the sifting of the [other] evidence
I could collect, and the latitude of the present church," combined
to make clear that this was indeed the exact point where the 1769
observations had been made. Davidson accordingly set up his
instruments and conducted his own observations on the same
spot.

These assignments, however, by no means exhausted his interest in the science of astronomy. On May 4, 1879, a highly significant entry appears in Davidson's diary, for on that day he records
having visited an elevated spot in the then sparsely settled district of San Francisco known as the Western Addition, where he
had "looked at the site for an observatory." This is the first
indication that he was planning such a move; it is also the
earliest known reference to what was to be the first astronomical
observatory on the west coast, an observatory over which he was
to preside for more than a quarter of a century.

The site he selected was in the area bounded by Washington,

Gough, Sacramento, and Laguna streets. Now a city park called Lafayette Square, in the early days it was popularly known as Holladay's Hill from the fact that on its crest—which Davidson carefully notes was 378 feet above sea level—stood the ornate wooden residence of Samuel W. Holladay, a well-known attorney and civic leader. When, in 1867, the San Francisco Board of Supervisors took over the surrounding area and added it to the municipal park system, Holladay successfully resisted all efforts to dislodge him. The consequence was that his clapboard "mansion," the timbers for which were said to have been brought round the Horn, stood for many years in lonely grandeur atop the hill. It was, in fact, not until the mid-1930's that it was eventually torn down and the site incorporated into the park.

Davidson's pioneer observatory, which long stood on city land adjacent to Holladay's holdings, has been described as a sturdy wooden building some fifteen feet square, the most conspicuous feature of which was a dome, about ten feet in diameter, set into its roof. Its scientific equipment consisted of a 6.4-inch refracting telescope and auxiliary instruments. Davidson not only used this in the protracted series of observations he over the years conducted there but from time to time he transported it on one or another of his astronomical assignments to distant points.

The Davidson Observatory, as it came to be known, was erected and equipped at his own expense. However, because many of the observations made there were in connection with his official work, the Survey for some years allotted Davidson a modest $120 annually to cover the cost of "carfare, repairs and other incidentals." Also, in 1880, the city authorities gave a degree of official recognition to the observatory by designating it the Lafayette Park Astronomical Station and stating that it was "devoted ... to the use of the Coast and Geodetic Survey as the standard telegraphic longitude station of the Pacific Coast."

At the time it was built, Davidson was listed in the San Francisco city directories as living at 777 Hyde Street, some little distance from Lafayette Park. Since it was his custom to spend several hours there nightly whenever weather conditions made observations possible, it is likely that when he came to select a site for a permanent residence the desire to be closer to the observatory had an important bearing on his ultimate decision. At any rate, the commodious wooden dwelling into which he and his family moved about 1885 stood at 2221 Washington Street near the corner of Laguna, and hence was only a few hundred feet from the observatory.

Throughout the two decades that followed he must have covered that distance many hundreds of times. For, except when his official duties necessitated his absence from the city, he could usually be found after nightfall seated at the telescope—sometimes in the early evening, at other times between the hours of midnight and dawn. This routine often went on without a break for weeks, during all of which time he, as head of operations on the coast, daily kept regular hours at the Survey's headquarters downtown.

In spite of the fact that his nightly observations commonly had to be made after he had spent a full day attending to his official duties, he did much valuable work there in the next two decades.

"An example of his untiring energy," wrote J. J. Gilbert in the *Bulletin* of the American Geographical Society for January, 1912, "was given when the question of the variation of latitude was mooted by astronomers, and the International Geodetic Association proposed a plan of systematic observations all around the world to test the question, Professor Davidson voluntarily undertook to assist in this and began systematic observations . . . in May, 1891. Every night, favorable for observations, during a period of fifteen months was devoted to this work."

Other results of his observations were reported in a lengthy series of lectures he delivered before members of the California Academy of Sciences and their guests, and which were subsequently printed in the Academy's *Proceedings* or *Bulletin,* or in the annual *Reports* of the Survey, or in the *Mining and Scientific Press.* Their scope and variety can best be indicated by listing the titles of a few of the papers: "Field Catalogue of 1,278 Time and Circumpolar Stars" (1885); "The Magnetic Variation at San Francisco" (1888), and "The Constant of Aberration as Determined from (6,786) Observations of Latitude at San Francisco" (1894).

Moreover, during the years he maintained the observatory, Davidson made its facilities available to local residents interested in astronomy, both fellow scientists with a professional knowledge in the subject and laymen curious to view the celestial bodies visible through its 6.4-inch telescope. Frequently, groups of students from the University of California and the San Francisco high schools gathered at the observatory at his invitation; to these he gave brief talks on astronomical theory and practice, and practical demonstrations of the uses to which the various instruments were put.

This firm belief that interest in such matters should always be encouraged was strikingly illustrated by an incident related by William Churchill soon after Davidson's death. One day in the mid-1890's word reached Davidson that an Oakland man, a butcher, had developed a keen interest in astronomy and in his basement was endeavoring to construct a home-made telescope and mounting in order to pursue his studies. Davidson forthwith hunted up the amateur, invited him to inspect his Lafayette Square observatory, and gave him valuable practical advice on how to build and set up his instruments. Davidson's interest, however, did not stop there. He presently brought the matter to the attention of an acquaintance, the Oakland capitalist and philanthropist Anthony Chabot. The result was that Chabot not only financed the building of the observatory that bears his name but installed the former butcher as its director. Churchill adds that the Chabot Observatory had an added distinction in that it was the first astronomical observatory to become an integral part of the public school system of an American city.

At the time of the earthquake and fire of 1906, when many thousands were rendered homeless, Davidson, as stated, made the Lafayette Square structure available as a shelter for women and children, after having first dismounted the telescope lest another severe shock dislodge it from its mountings and so endanger the refugees. This was one of the last uses to which the little building was put. For by the early 1900's Davidson's eyesight had begun to fail, and presently became so bad that the astronomical observations in which he had been steadily engaged for well over half a century had to be drastically curtailed and finally abandoned entirely. Accordingly, about 1907, the historic observatory, the first of its kind on the coast, was permanently shut down.

XIII · james lick

Important as was the work carried on in Lafayette Square, Davidson's major contribution to astronomy lay in quite another direction; that is, in the part he played in the founding of the famous Lick Observatory, which, upon its completion in 1888, was widely heralded as the world's most useful instrumentality in that field of science.

That Davidson, more than any other man, was responsible for turning the thoughts of the eccentric San Francisco millionaire James Lick into such channels, and for giving the donor sound practical advice during the period the project was in its formative stages, has long been recognized by those familiar with the circumstances surrounding its origin and early history.

Many years later, Davidson published, in the *University of California Magazine* for April, 1899, a reminiscent article in which he recalled his association with Lick and the steps by which the great telescope became a reality. By that account, the two men first met in February, 1873, when Davidson and another official of the California Academy of Sciences called on the capitalist in his cluttered room in the Lick House to thank him for his unexpected and entirely unsolicited gift to the Academy of a valuable 80-foot lot on Market Street.

That visit was the first of many, for the seventy-seven-year-old former piano maker had become deeply interested in the scientific activities of the Academy and urged its president to return and discuss them with him. Davidson relates that in the course of these talks Lick developed a consuming curiosity about astronomy, and that moreover he showed a considerable grasp of its principles, although he had "never looked through a telescope or read a work on astronomy."

In the weeks that followed, while propped up in bed in his hotel room, the capitalist listened closely while Davidson dilated on the objects revealed through the powerful instruments of the astronomers, of the rings of Saturn, the belts of Jupiter, and the mountains and depressions on the sterile surface of the moon. On one occasion Lick's interest was aroused to the point that he urged his visitor to provide him with a telescope so that he could view these wonders from the window of his room.

Uppermost in the mind of the aged and ill man at the time was the question of the disposition of his estate, the value of which was conservatively fixed at $3,000,000. Since he had no near relatives—except for an illegitimate son, to whom he planned to leave $10,000—it was his wish that the bulk of his fortune be devoted to philanthropic ends. Before he and Davidson met he had made two substantial gifts of property in the downtown area, as stated earlier: one to the California Academy of Sciences, the other to the Society of California Pioneers. He was then considering a variety of other plans, one of which—happily it never materialized—was to erect a vast stone pyramid, "higher than those of the Egyptians," which was to cover an entire block in the center of the city.

However, as a result of his newly aroused interest in astronomy, Lick presently decided to provide funds for the manufacture and housing of a great telescope, which he insisted must be "superior to and more powerful than any telescope yet made." According to Davidson, his original plan was to install this instrument on a plot of land at Fourth and Market streets, adjacent to the property deeded to the Academy and the pioneers' society. He also proposed to place three elaborate statuary groups on the same site: one in memory of the author of "The Star-Spangled Banner," a second honoring Thomas Paine (of whose writings he was an ardent admirer), and a third honoring himself or his father and mother. It was with difficulty that Davidson persuaded Lick to locate the observatory elsewhere. "It took," he recalled, "several months of quiet but persistent presentation of facts to demonstrate the advantage of great elevation for astronomical observation." A number of other sites were then considered: in the mountains overlooking his Santa Clara mill site, on the crest of Mount Saint Helena at the upper end of the Napa Valley, and on the shores of Lake Tahoe.

From the beginning, Davidson urged that the observatory be built high in the Sierra, his reason being that at high altitudes conditions for astronomical observations were superior to those prevailing at lower levels. This was a theory on which he had earlier commented at length in correspondence with Coast Survey Superintendent Benjamin Peirce, and he had further developed it in a paper entitled "Astronomical Observations on the Sierra Nevada," which was published in the 1872 *Report* of the Survey.

Incidentally, the question whether high or moderate altitudes are more desirable for such observations has long been a matter

of debate. Years later, Professor W. W. Campbell, then head of
Lick Observatory, after writing that "there can be no doubt that
Davidson's advice was invaluable in giving the [observatory]
project a practical turn at times . . . when the entire proposal
might have been wrecked on the rocks of impracticability," went
on to state: "But on the score of altitude . . . the consensus of
opinion among those who have used great telescopes and are
experienced in the work of great observatories, is to the effect
that Lick's eventual choice of a medium altitude was wise."

For a time, however, it appeared that Davidson's recommendation that the telescope be located on a Sierra mountaintop had
been adopted. "Finally," he wrote, "on the 20th of October,
1873, he permitted me to announce to the California Academy
of Sciences that the observatory would be placed in the Sierra
Nevada at an elevation of 10,000 feet." This announcement—
which Davidson made at the conclusion of his lecture before
Academy members and their guests on the subject of "Spectrum
Analysis"—was the first intimation the public had received of
Lick's contemplated gift. The news was prominently displayed
in all the local journals the following day; the *Alta California*'s
column-long story on its front page bore this heading: "The
Lick Observatory. The Greatest Scientific Work of America
About to be Commenced," and the text quoted Davidson's re-
marks of the previous evening.

The project as originally planned well deserved such head-
lines. For Lick, having decided to allot a major share of his
fortune to that end, was determined that the observatory to bear
his name must far surpass any then in existence or planned. On
being informed that the largest reflector then in use was three
feet in diameter, he directed that his be made "twice as big."
Since a glass of that size with the attendant equipment necessary
to house and operate it would have been immensely costly, Davidson applied himself to convincing the donor of the necessity of
scaling down the magnitude of his conception. This evidently

proved no easy task, for Davidson later wrote that "it took him [Lick] a long time to bring himself to agree to even a 40-inch objective." At that time a 40-inch glass was deemed impractical by many authorities; however, Davidson, while on a trip east the following year, obtained the promise of Alvin Clark of Cambridge, Massachusetts, the country's foremost maker of telescopic lenses, to undertake to grind them "if Feil & Co., of Paris, could cast perfect discs of that size."

For several years before the news of Lick's gift was made public, Davidson had been looking ahead to the day when an observatory of the first rank would be erected in the West. This is made clear by his correspondence with the Coast Survey headquarters in Washington. On February 1, 1869, he thus wrote Superintendent Peirce from San Francisco: "I have been feeling the ground in this community among men likely to be interested about the establishment of a large observatory on this coast, with the completest outfit of instruments, observers, means of publication, etc." He went on to state his belief that "we have a climate here which will prove exceptionally good for astronomical observations," and added: "At my mountain stations I have observed stars of the 6th magnitude with a telescope that would not see the 7th in New England stations."

In the same letter he asked Peirce—himself a distinguished astronomer—to give him "an idea of the cost of such an undertaking . . . the relative amounts of the items of erection of buildings, cost of instruments, expenses of Superintendent and observers, cost of publication, etc." Then, when he was on the east coast in 1874, he conferred with authorities both at Harvard and at the United States Naval Observatory in Washington, gathering data on the probable cost of a huge observatory such as Lick desired; their estimates were that it would require an expenditure of approximately $1,500,000.

This sum was far in excess of what Lick had planned to spend. Originally, he had limited his bequest to half a million dollars, and Davidson had set about the task of persuading him to increase that amount. In this he evidently had some success, for on June 14, 1874, on the eve of his departure on his trip to Japan and on round the world, this brief entry appears in his diary: "At 12:45 called on Mr. Lick; found him very cordial. Said he had added $200,000 after my telling him $500,000 was too small. Said if well enough he would start with me around the world tomorrow."

Thus when details of the trust fund Lick had set up were made public on July 16, 1874, it was learned that of the nearly $2,000,000 to be expended, the largest single amount, $700,000, was earmarked to finance the observatory, the founding of which, moreover, was to take precedence over his other benefactions.

A board of San Franciscans prominent in civic affairs was appointed to administer the Lick Trust. However, the philanthropist, who then was seventy-eight and was understandably eager to see work on the observatory begin promptly, soon became impatient at what he considered the dilatoriness of his appointees. Accordingly, on March 27, 1875, he revoked the trust and some months later executed a new deed and named a new board of trustees. This second group evidently proved no more satisfactory to Lick than the first, for on September 4, 1876, only a few weeks before his death, he again revoked the trust and appointed a third board.

Davidson, who was absent on his world tour when Lick appointed the boards of trustees, learned on his return to San Francisco that certain decisions with which he was not in sympathy had been made in regard to the observatory. One was the rejection of his recommendation that it be located in the Sierra at an altitude of 10,000 feet or more. Another was Lick's refusal to increase his bequest to $1,200,000, which Davidson considered the minimum amount that would be needed. In his reminiscent paper written years later, he thus explains the reasons that caused him to withdraw from further connection with the project: "When

Mr. Lick again changed his views and named Mt. Hamilton as the site and cut down the $1,200,000 to $700,000, I showed him that such a sum was insufficient . . . At a subsequent interview, I declined further conference and responsibility in advising him, despite his urgency for me to stand by him."

However, notwithstanding his disappointment that on two important points his advice had been disregarded, Davidson retained a great deal of respect for Lick's liberal contributions to scientific research, and indeed a genuine liking for the man himself. In one of their many discussions of the observatory project, Davidson remarked, half-seriously, that the founder might appropriately be buried at the observatory, directly beneath the great telescope that was to bear his name. Somewhat to Davidson's surprise, the other at once approved the idea and stated that he would so specify in his will. When, however, Davidson suggested that if that plan were carried out, it would be simpler to direct that his body be cremated and his ashes deposited beneath the telescope, the doughty invalid's reply was prompt and emphatic: "No, sir!" he retorted. "I intend to rot like a gentleman!"

At the time of the old man's death, on October 1, 1876, construction of the observatory had not yet begun, and his body was interred in a San Francisco cemetery. However, some eleven years later, that provision of his will was belatedly carried out. On January 9, 1887, his remains were sealed in the base of the pier supporting the great telescope on the crest of Mount Hamilton.

Although Davidson withdrew from the project while it was still in its preliminary stages, it was—and is—generally recognized that in its conception and early planning he played a role second only to that of the donor himself. Years later, near the end of the century, when the office of director of the observatory became vacant, a vigorous campaign was launched to have the seventy-three-year-old Davidson appointed to the post, and when the Regents of the University of California, which had accepted the property on its completion in 1888, chose a younger man for the position there was a great deal of adverse comment in some of the most influential journals of the state.

XIV · widening horizons

On his return to the west coast in 1876 after his trip round the world, Davidson resumed direction of the Survey's extensive operations in the huge area under his jurisdiction.

Among the major accomplishments of the next fifteen years was the laying out of the two long base lines, one in the northern part of the state and the other in the southern part, on which the primary triangulation of much of California was based. Authorities have highly praised the accuracy of these surveys, one stating that they "stand higher than any ever executed in America, Europe, or India." Of their importance, Charles B. Davenport, writing in 1937 in a *Biographical Memoir* of the National Academy of Sciences, stated: "One of the greatest achievements of Davidson, almost equal to his definitive survey charts of the Pacific Coast . . . was his measurement of the base lines upon which all distances in the extensive triangulation of the State of California depend. The first was the Yolo base line measured twice by him in 1881 and [the second] the Los Angeles base line measured three times in 1888–89."

Another of Davidson's important assignments in these years was that of locating precisely the boundary between California and Nevada. The northern part of this line, from the Oregon border to Lake Tahoe, following the 120th meridian, was fixed by him in 1872, and the 405-mile diagonal, extending from the lake to the Colorado River, was surveyed and marked under his direction in 1893. The accurate location of this last-named section of the boundary involved many difficulties, not only because of the barren and rugged nature of the territory through which the line passes but because at each end it terminates in water.

All through the 1870's and 1880's Davidson by preference continued to spend with his survey parties in the field as much time as could be spared from his administrative duties. Thus, many of his letters and reports of the period are written not from the San Francisco suboffice but from points on the long shoreline where work was currently in progress or from stations in the High Sierra where triangulation or astronomical observations were being conducted.

In the meantime, as has been indicated, his growing renown as a leader in his profession had come to be widely recognized, not only in the West but farther afield. The consequence was that with increasing frequency he was detached from his regular duties and delegated to carry out special assignments in related fields. Some of the earlier of these have been mentioned: his geographic reconnaissance and economic survey of Alaska in 1867 while negotiations for the purchase of that territory were in progress; his inspection of the weights and measures at the San Francisco and Philadelphia mints; and his astronomical expeditions to Alaska in 1869 to observe a total solar eclipse, to Lower California, to New Mexico, and, in 1874, to Japan to view a transit of Venus, from which place he continued round the world, studying irrigation and conservation methods in many countries.

These, however, by no means exhaust the list of his special duties in those crowded years. In 1873 he was appointed by President Grant one of a three-man advisory committee to conduct a survey of the harbor of San Francisco and recommend improvements. He and his two associates, Admiral John Rogers,

U.S.N., and Colonel George H. Mendell of the Corps of Engineers, U.S.A., after a thorough investigation, prepared a report of their findings, which was published in 1876. Two years later he was sent to the Paris Exposition "to examine the instruments of precision applicable to geodesy and astronomy," and while there he was made chairman of an international jury charged with judging "the moving power of machinery." In performing its duties, the jury examined some 3,800 mechanical appliances and awarded 850 prizes, and Davidson was given a medal and a diploma by the French government in recognition of his services.

In 1886 the San Francisco Board of Supervisors commissioned him to make a survey of the sewerage system of the city—which, incidentally, he found so unsatisfactory that in his report he stated that in all his travels he had found but one other community where the means of sewage disposal was "in such a deplorably low condition." Two years later, in 1888, President Cleveland made him a member of the Mississippi River Commission, and the following year President Harrison appointed him official delegate of the United States to a meeting of the International Geographical Association in Paris, at which time the Secretary of State "designated him bearer of the international prototypes of the standard metre and kilogramme from Paris to Washington." While abroad on that mission he again visited the leading observatories and makers of scientific instruments of Europe in order to keep abreast with the latest advances in these fields.

He was by nature of an inventive turn of mind, and throughout his long connection with the Survey he was ever on the lookout for means of improving the methods employed in its work and of enhancing the effectiveness of the instruments then in use. Both in his official reports and in his informal correspondence with the successive superintendents of the bureau, he made frequent reference to such matters, usually to point out how procedures might be changed for the better, or the equipment used in surveying, offshore soundings, or astronomical observations rendered more efficient. Thus, during his first years in California—a land where violent earth movements were much more frequent than on the east coast—we find him, as stated earlier, writing Superintendent Bache that he was at work on a device intended to record the duration and intensity of earthquakes.

Some ten years later, in 1867, he perfected an appliance which became known as the Davidson Meridian Instrument, and which subsequently for many years was widely used in the work of the Survey. In 1874 he devised an improved clamp for use on astronomical and geodetic instruments, and two years later, a device termed "a new break-circuit chronometer." This was presently followed by what was described as a highly ingenious and useful "microscopic method of determining irregularities of micrometer screws." These, together with a number of improvements to scientific instruments used in surveys and astronomical work, he consistently refused to have patented, preferring, as he stated, to make them available without restriction to fellow workers in these fields.

Much of his voluminous writing on technical subjects bears on this phase of his interests. Among these might be mentioned a paper entitled "Sextant with Attached Spirit Level Horizon," published in the *Journal* of the Franklin Institute in 1865; "New Meridian Instrument for Time, Latitude, and Azimuth," Appendix 8 of the Coast Survey *Report* for 1867; "On an Improved Leveling Rod," in the *Mining and Scientific Press*, September 1, 1873; and, in 1892, an article in the Coast Survey *Report* (Part 2, Appendix 9) bearing this comprehensive title: "Measurement of the Irregularity in One Turn of the Micrometer Screw and the Relative Value of Each Turn."

In the early 1880's Davidson became engaged in a scientific investigation which, though it was outside the field of his official duties, interested him deeply, as it did indeed virtually every resident of the coast, scientist and layman alike. What appeared to be a highly important discovery had been made in the field of paleontology: the uncovering on the grounds of the Nevada State Prison at Carson City of a group of footprints, together with fossils, shells, and fragments of bones and tusks. These had been brought to light some twenty feet below the surface while excavations were being made at the prison quarry. Among the animal tracks identified were those of elk, horses, dogs, tigers, bears, and other species still extant. Particular interest was aroused by what seemed to be the huge footprints of some long-vanished elephantlike creature, which was referred to as either a mastodon or a mammoth.

Even more sensational, however, were certain markings that some early visitors to the spot declared had been made by a prehistoric man—an opinion that the journalists who had hurried to the scene naturally did not fail to play up in dispatches to their papers. This theory, of course, aroused much interest. In the days that followed, discussion pro and con about the authenticity of these supposed relics of what had come to be called the "Carson Giant"—for the much-debated prints were some twenty inches long and correspondingly broad—grew steadily in volume and vehemence.

The interest of scientists in the matter was fully as keen as that of the general public, and leading anthropologists of the coast and specialists in allied fields hastened to the scene, carefully scrutinized the prints, and in due time issued reports of their findings. Among these were two eminent Californians, Dr. H. W. Harkness, who later succeeded Davidson as president of the California Academy of Sciences, and Joseph LeConte, professor of geology, zoölogy, and botany at the University of California.

As one of the leading scientific societies on the coast, the California Academy had, of course, a special interest in the Carson City discoveries. Its board of trustees promptly authorized Davidson and one other member to proceed to the spot and make an examination. Accordingly, he and his companion, together with an eastern scientist who chanced to be in San Francisco, visited the prison and spent several days as guests of the warden while they carefully measured the footprints, made casts of some of them, studied their shapes and positions, and closely examined the geological formation in which they had been found.

At the August 6, 1883, meeting of the Academy, Davidson gave an account of their findings. His address was considered of such wide importance that it was printed in its entirety in the September 8 and 15 issues of the *Mining and Scientific Press* and subsequently was reissued in pamphlet form. In it, although he agreed with other scientists who had examined the markings that the discovery was an important one, and urged that further excavations be made in the hope of turning up additional evidence, he took a markedly skeptical view of the theory that any of the prints had been made by a human being. It was his opinion that the much-debated marks had been impressed into the mud of an ancient lake shore by a quadruped, "Whether a megatheroid or a bear I leave for the paleontologists to say." This conclusion he based mainly on the fact that in most instances where the prints were visible they were found in pairs, usually with one superimposed on the other, as those of walking four-footed animals normally would be.

"In this light," he concluded, "the evidence seems to me unanswerable that the so-called man was a quadruped, and it will require the wiping out of these duplications before they can be assigned to a biped." In the face of that argument, the theory that the footprints were of human origin seems to have collapsed, for soon afterward, stories and speculation about the "Carson Giant" disappeared permanently from the columns of the coast newspapers.

XV · place names

One phase of Davidson's professional duties in which from the beginning he took a special interest was the conferring of appropriate names on the mountains, headlands, coves, and other geographical features of the long coastline where, from 1850 onward for forty-five years, he conducted surveys.

All during the early part of his stay in the West this was a highly necessary function. For when he first arrived, and indeed for many years thereafter, large sections of the shoreline had never before been explored in detail, and in mapping such areas and preparing charts for navigators he often found it necessary to confer identifying names on certain landmarks that had thereto been nameless, or on those that had been christened by one or another of the early explorers but with the passage of the years had lost their original designations.

To that work Davidson seems from the first to have brought not only sound judgment but a conscientious regard for the historical and other elements involved. This was by no means a simple task, particularly in California, which had long been ruled by Spain and Mexico, and where the same place sometimes bore four different designations, given successively by the native Indians, the early explorers, the Spanish settlers, and, after 1848, by the Americans.

In preparing the Survey's charts, Davidson faced the necessity of bringing order out of this confusion. He accordingly adopted a general policy which he applied not only to California but to other places on the coast. "I have believed," he wrote in 1907, "in retaining and in applying all the old Spanish names; and have utilized Indian names when they were descriptive, and would use them all through Alaska where the prospector may need the services of native guides." He stated that "for the last half-century I have used my best endeavors to identify and restore old Spanish names to important locations along this western coast from Cape San Lucas to Mt. St. Elias."

This concern for the retention of the names applied to coastal points by the Indians, Spaniards, and first explorers was in all likelihood the origin of Davidson's abiding interest in the early history of the region, and particularly in the voyages of the pioneer navigators. His extended researches in connection with these early voyages continued for many years, with the result that at the time of his death he was generally recognized as the foremost authority on the subject. Moreover, there can be little doubt that but for his services in that connection, notably in the 1850's when the first Survey charts were published and came into general use, the melodious Spanish names of numerous California headlands, inlets, mountains, and other coastal landmarks would have been permanently discarded.

Commenting on that phase of his work, Henry R. Wagner, himself long a student of the voyages of the early explorers of the Pacific Coast, wrote in 1932:

The proper names of localities were [in 1855] giving a great deal of trouble to the Coast Survey. He [Davidson] considered that it was of the greatest importance to trace the history of discovery on the coast, to ascertain the original and the successive names of places, and to go back to the earlier ones when the later ones had not become too permanently attached to the locality. His aim was to make the Coast Survey maps and charts the standards for names and their spelling, as well as for the geography of the country.

In this undertaking he had, during the first sixteen years on the coast, the warm support of the Survey's chief, Alexander Bache; and their correspondence throughout that period frequently touches on this subject. Thus, in 1852, while Davidson was engaged in surveys in Washington Territory on the southern shore of the Strait of Juan de Fuca, he wrote to Bache urging—successfully as it proved—that the Indian name of Neah Bay be applied to one of the coastal inlets. This is but one of many instances in which his recommendations concerning the naming of geographical places from the Mexican border to Alaska were officially adopted.

This process of restoring the original names to coastal landmarks was, as indicated, frequently a complicated one, calling not only for a painstaking examination of the narratives and charts of the early navigators but involving knotty problems in the matter of orthography, which often showed wide variations on different maps. On this phase of the subject, Davidson, as late as 1895, wrote Henry Gannett, chairman of the U. S. Board on Geographic Names, which since its establishment in 1890 had been the final authority on place names in the country. "No reliance whatever," he stated, "can be placed upon the spelling of proper names in Mexico-Spanish California. . . . Years ago when I was first looking for the Spanish geographical and personal names among the Mexican grants and other documents I found even the proper names of persons spelled differently in the same documents. . . . I found for Sausalito ten or twelve spellings and for Bonita four or five, to say nothing of different names applied to the same locality. . . ."

In addition to these difficulties, it frequently fell to Davidson to confer identifying names on localities that had theretofore been nameless, or the former designations of which had either been lost or were duplicated by others in the same general area. Of these perhaps the most widely known today are those on the shore of Puget Sound and on the Olympic Peninsula which, as previously mentioned, he named in memory of Robert H. Fauntleroy, under whom he had served on the Gulf of Mexico, and for Fauntleroy's four children, one of whom, Ellinor, Davidson later married.

However, the important place Davidson today occupies in the nomenclature of the coast is due not alone to the names he himself applied to many of its localities but to the fact that his own name has been conferred on a variety of its topographical features in commemoration of his long services in the area. Thus, although during the half century that has passed since his death in 1911 his highly valuable contributions to the mapping of the west coast—and indeed his very name—have become virtually unknown to the public at large, it must not be assumed that his services are doomed to be permanently forgotten, for at numerous points along the coast, from California to the remote Aleutians, there exist memorials to his life and achievements that will serve to preserve his memory for generations to come. These are, of course, the many geographical features, both on land and in the sea, that today bear his name. Indeed, it has been said that the number of such honors bestowed on him within this region exceeds that of any other man.

At any rate, even a casual examination of the maps and charts of the Pacific Coast will reveal that the name Davidson has been given to a wide variety of its physical features. These range from a historic mountain in western Nevada to a great Alaskan glacier, and include not only inlets, promontories, rocks, and other coastal points but a large mountain range in central Alaska, an ocean current, and a vast submarine plateau, called the Davidson Seamount, which lies many miles off the California coast.

One of the most widely known of the localities bearing his name is Mount Davidson in San Francisco, the highest point in the city. This elevation, lying in a now closely built residential district to the south of Twin Peaks, was first surveyed by Davidson in the early 1860's and was long known as Blue Mountain.

In 1911, however, a few weeks after his death, the Board of Supervisors officially renamed it in memory of him. The Sierra Club, the old-established mountaineering society, of which Davidson had long been a member, had taken a leading part in bringing this about, and John Muir, its president, had been scheduled to make an address at the formal dedication exercises. However, the day proved to be a stormy one, and this prevented the venerable Muir from attending. His place was taken by the club's vice-president, Alexander McAdie, chief of the San Francisco weather bureau and himself a scientist of note.

"I remember the Sunday . . . when Mount Davidson was named," wrote McAdie's widow long after. "Alec was to make the address and name it. It was one of those hopelessly drizzly days. Alec went bravely on, though he met no one on the way— across cabbage-patches and what-not. No one ever did come—but Alec christened the peak." Some twenty-eight years later, on December 20, 1929, the 25-acre wooded area about the mountain's crest was dedicated as a city park. On the summit a huge cross was erected. Sunrise Easter services held about its base the following March inaugurated a civic tradition that yearly draws thousands on a pilgrimage to the spot.

Two other Mount Davidsons exist, both named for the scientist. One is a peak in the Virginia Range of Nevada, close to the California border, about the sides of which once clustered the populous towns of the Comstock lode, for during the 1860's and 1870's the region was one of the largest producers of silver in the entire history of mining. Known as Sun Mountain to the thousands drawn there after the first claims were located in 1859, it was later rechristened Mount Davidson. Precisely why Davidson's name was given to this dominant peak of the area is not known with certainty. One version is that it was in commemoration of his work in surveying the California-Nevada boundary line, which was begun in 1873; another states merely that the name was given "because he made an accurate measurement of the mountain." Some early Virginia City writers, however, have stated that Sun Peak was renamed not for George Davidson but for one Donald Davidson, the San Francisco representative, in the early 1860's, of the European banking house of the Roths- childs, who soon after the discovery of silver there had tried— unsuccessfully, as it proved—to interest the parent firm in finan- cing the development of certain of the mines. Those who put forth that claim, however, offered no evidence of any kind to support it, and it is now quite generally agreed that the honor rightfully belongs to George Davidson.

Regarding the third of the three mountains bearing his name there is no question whom it is intended to honor. This is a peak on the south side of Sanborn Harbor, on Nagai, a 32-mile-long island of the Shumagin group off the Alaskan peninsula that extends westward from the mainland toward Siberia. It was so named in 1872 by the naturalist William Healey Dall, long a member of the Coast Survey, who from 1871 to 1884 was in charge of its work on the Alaska coast and in the Aleutians, and whose book, *Alaska and Its Resources,* was long a standard work on that region.

Alaska, with the early survey and exploration of which David- son was closely identified, today has a number of other physical features that bear his name. Perhaps the best known of these is the Davidson Glacier, which was so designated by Superintend- ent Bache in 1867 in recognition of Davidson's services as head of the party sent north that year to survey the resources, climate, and topography of the territory. Of the grandeur of that broad frozen river, which flows into the sea on the west side of the mouth of Chilkat Inlet, between Juneau and Skagway, John Muir thus commented in the mid-1880's in a letter to his—and David- son's—friend, the California landscape artist William Keith: "Very imposing is Davidson Glacier, named, as you know, for our own Governor Davidson, nearly twenty years ago. From a great height it pours down, a frozen cataract . . . between two

granite mountains and shoulders. . . . You will never forget it."
In 1869 a headland adjacent to the glacier was likewise given his
name and today appears on charts and maps as Point Davidson.

Other Alaska localities that perpetuate his name are Davidson
Inlet, in the Prince of Wales Archipelago, which was so named
in 1869 by William Healey Dall, who later christened the Mount
Davidson on Nagai Island; Davidson Bank, near Unimak Pass
in the Aleutians, named by the U. S. Fish Commission in 1888;
and the Davidson Range, a mountain region which comprises the
northeastern part of the extensive Brooks Range in northern
Alaska bordering on the Arctic Ocean. This was named in 1900
by Captain John Turner, when he was making a survey of the
Alaska-Canada boundary.

Points elsewhere that bear Davidson's name are a submerged
reef in Rosario Strait, which he discovered in 1854 and named
Entrance Rock, but which later appeared on British charts as
Davidson Rock and has so remained; and, far to the north, a
promontory situated on Victoria Strait, near Queen Maud Gulf,
which was christened Davidson Point in honor of his friend by
the famed polar explorer Roald Amundsen.

Of the many points on the western and northern coasts of the
continent on which his name has been conferred the most recent
is the Davidson Seamount, which was officially so designated by
the U. S. Board on Geographical Names in 1938. The board's
description and citation reads: "Davidson Seamount: a submarine elevation in mountain form, which rises from a depth of
1900 fathoms to within 729 fathoms of the surface, near lat.
35°43′30″ N., long. 122°43′10″ W., about 75 miles west of Point
Piedras Blancas, California, in the Pacific Ocean. Named in
honor of George Davidson (1825–1911) of the U. S. Coast and
Geodetic Survey who, as chief of party and later in charge of all
Coast Survey operations on the Pacific Coast, was active in charting the waters of the west coast." This note adds: "The generic
term 'seamount' is here used for the first time, and is applied to

submarine elevations of mountain form whose character and depth are such that the existing terms bank, shoal, pinnacle, etc., are not appropriate."

Although Davidson's primary work with the Survey was the accurate fixing of the positions of headlands, harbors, mountains, and other geographical features of the Pacific shoreline, he had as well a deep interest in the hydrographic surveys that were simultaneously being carried out. All through the early years he and his parties in progressing from station to station had traveled, as stated, almost entirely by water, there being no roads or trails over most of the area, and while the ship was close inshore it was his habit, in his own words, "to have the weighted line in hand" and with it make frequent soundings.

This resulted in his interest being drawn to the characteristics of the ocean currents near the shore, and in turn led to his discovery of what presently became known as the Davidson Inshore Eddy Current. In a paper published by the Coast and Geodetic Survey in 1918, written by its then superintendent, E. Lester Jones, the following passage deals with the discovery and characteristics of this hitherto unknown water movement:

> Professor George Davidson, for many years an officer of the Coast and Geodetic Survey, . . . devoted a great deal of study to the subject of coastwise currents. As a result of such study, Professor Davidson concluded that there existed, from 50 to 100 miles offshore, a southerly setting current of unknown width and velocity, and that inside of this, following closely along the general trend of the coast, was a northerly setting current . . . He had observed such northerly setting currents at various anchorages while engaged on survey work along the coast, and had also ascertained that logs of the redwood (which does not grow north of California) were frequently found on the shores of Washington, British Columbia, and even Alaska, the wood being well known to the natives of these regions. Obviously, the only way such logs could have reached these shores was by being carried there by the currents.

Superintendent Jones added that although data then available (in 1918) concerning the speed and direction of the Davidson In-

shore Current were still incomplete, "certain characteristics have
been noted which it is important that the navigator should have in
mind, as they may materially assist him in avoiding disaster."

And finally, in the field of geodesy, his name was applied to
the Davidson Quadrilaterals. These, which formed the basis of
the extensive triangulation surveys by which the locations of
scores of prominent geographical positions, both along the shoreline and in the interior, were determined, were mainly founded
on two primary base lines, one in the Sacramento Valley and the
other in southern California. The importance of these base lines,
and the painstaking care with which they were measured, have
been noted by numerous authorities. Thus the *Columbia Encyclo-
pedia* states: "He measured the great base lines, known as the
'Davidson Quadrilaterals,' upon which the primary triangulation
of the Pacific Coast states is based." Ruliff S. Holway, writing in
the *University of California Chronicle* of January, 1912, com-
ments on their value and extreme accuracy, and Charles B.
Davenport's *Biographical Memoir of George Davidson* (Washington: National Academy of Sciences, 1937) pronounces this
"one of his greatest achievements."

Both the Yolo and Los Angeles base lines were nearly eleven
miles in length—longer than any similar lines that had hitherto
been laid out. Since the accuracy of computations based on them
depended on their precise measurement, the lines had to be measured with extreme care. In January, 1889, upon the completion
of his work on the Los Angeles line, Davidson wrote his sister in
Philadelphia that he had been engaged in that task "seventeen to
eighteen hours daily for three months." After stating that the
$10\frac{3}{4}$-mile distance had been measured three times, he added that
the "second measurement differed from the first by one-third
inch; the third differed one one-hundred and twentieth of an inch
from the second." The measurement of the Yolo base line was
done with equal care and precision, a report of the Coast Survey
fixing the probable margin of error in that 10.8-mile distance at

"about one ten-thousandth of one percent." Thus, these two lines, on which so much of the triangulation of California was based, were properly named in recognition of the care and high technical skill of the man who laid them out.

In the list of objects bearing Davidson's name, one final entry should be made—this one in a quite different field of science. In 1937 Charles B. Davenport wrote that " 'an extinct whale from California,' discovered by Professor E. D. Cope near San Diego, was named Eschrichitus davidsonii."

It will occur to many that there was something singularly appropriate about that designation.

XVI · dismissal from the survey

In the summer of 1895 Davidson's long connection with the Coast and Geodetic Survey, which had begun a full half century earlier, was abruptly terminated. His dismissal came, as he himself stated at the time, as a complete surprise to him, as it did also to his friends and associates both in California and elsewhere. Two years later, in 1897, in commenting on the circumstances of his removal, Davidson wrote: "On the 30th of June, Superintendent Duffield transmitted the letter of Secretary Carlisle informing me that my services would no longer be required. I was not informed whether any charges had been made against me officially or otherwise and do not today know the cause of my removal."

At the time it was widely believed that political considerations alone had brought about his dismissal, an opinion that seems to have been shared by later writers on the subject. It was a time of financial stringency throughout the nation, and rigid economy in all governmental expenditures was the watchword of the incoming administration. The Coast Survey did not escape, for soon after President Cleveland took office for his second term in 1893 there came, in the words of a writer in *Science*, "a return of the hostile spirit in the Survey." This account continues: "The then chief, Dr. T. C. Mendenhall, was harshly treated by the new Secretary of Treasury, John G. Carlisle. Mendenhall resigned and was succeeded by General Duffield, a civil engineer. Duffield . . . advised Congress to reduce the field force by twenty percent after nine weeks in office. The bill made necessary the retirement of four assistants."

The *Science* article adds: "Among those dismissed was Professor George Davidson, sound in health, active in his mind and the most distinguished member of the scientific force of the Bureau, a man of international reputation and the staunchest reliance of every superintendent from Bache to Mendenhall."

In a volume entitled *Centennial Celebration of the United States Coast and Geodetic Survey*, published by the Department of Commerce in 1916, reference to that troubled era is made in these words:

A . . . regrettable state of affairs prevailed during a considerable period of the administration of General William Ward Duffield, who served as Superintendent for about three years following his appointment in the autumn of 1894. Not only was the influence of the spoilsman again paramount, but for some unexplainable reason a number of men were dismissed from the force whose places could not be filled from any source whatever. Men of long and faithful service whose reputation was international were lost to the Survey at that time, though a few were afterwards reappointed. It is charitable to assume that the Superintendent, who was by profession a civil engineer with a record of good service in the Civil War, had passed the years of discretion before receiving his appointment. . . . The historian would gladly pass over these unpleasant episodes, but a due regard for the good name and fame of many individuals involved demands this brief reference to them.

Elsewhere in the same book it is recorded that after the abrupt dismissal of Davidson and other eminent members of the staff, "the mathematicians and physicists of the country protested so violently that Duffield was removed on November 20, 1897."

General Duffield's dismissal took place toward the end of President Cleveland's term in office, and although Davidson was then past seventy, a concerted movement got under way to have him appointed superintendent by the incoming administration. Numerous influential Californians rallied to his support and endorsed his candidacy. David Starr Jordan, president of Stanford University and himself a noted scientist, referred to Davidson's dismissal as "the recent affront which politics has given science," and urged his appointment. California's senior senator, George C. Perkins, was particularly active in his behalf, stating that he had been "most unfairly treated" by the former administration, having "been fired without a single day's notice or a word of commendation for the public service he had rendered." To Davidson, the outspoken senator wrote that plans were afoot, in the event Davidson was not given the post as the Survey's chief, to have Congress pass a bill at its next session placing him on the retired list with a pension on a par with army officers of the same rank, and adding: "We will also take it upon ourselves to see that Superintendent Duffield's salary is cut down to $1000 a year, which is about $900 more than he is worth."

Ralph C. Harrison, Associate Justice of the California Supreme Court, joined in the campaign and thus wrote the new U. S. Attorney General, Joseph McKenna: "He was removed from his position during the last administration for no other than political reasons," and recommended his appointment. In San Francisco a petition was drawn up endorsing his candidacy, and this was signed by many citizens prominent in the political, commercial, and scientific circles of the city. One paragraph of this document, taking cognizance of the fact that the candidate's advanced years—he was then seventy-two—might be considered a liability in some quarters, read thus: "As there has been some question raised as to Professor Davidson's age, we desire to call attention to the fact that there is no man more active physically and mentally . . . and we believe the ripe experience he has gained by his long service renders him all the more capable for the position."

It is clear that many of those who in 1897 urged his appointment did so not only because they believed him well qualified for the post but because of their indignation at the manner of his dismissal two years earlier. It seemed but just that he be vindicated by being made chief of the bureau from which he had been unceremoniously ousted. That the resentment his dismissal had aroused in scientific circles on the west coast and farther afield was not soon forgotten is clear from a paper on Davidson's career published in the *Proceedings* of the California Academy of Sciences soon after his death nearly two decades later. "That this man," the writer concludes, "after fifty years of faithful service, a service that called forth unstinted admiration and honors from all maritime nations, should have been treated by his own government as if he were an ordinary laborer, hired for a day's work and then dropped without excuse or warning, is one of the things for which Americans have often had to hang their heads in shame."

However, the spirited efforts of his friends and fellow scientists to secure for him the appointment ended in failure. It is said that although his candidacy was carefully considered by the authorities in Washington, his age counted strongly against him and resulted in the selection of a younger man. In any event, on December 1, 1897, Henry Smith Pritchett, a noted astronomer and educator, who was more than thirty years Davidson's junior, was appointed to the post; and he filled it with distinction for the next three years.

Although the efforts to have Davidson named chief of the bureau he had served so long thus proved fruitless, there is no evidence that this outcome greatly disappointed him. He was, for one thing, much too busy to waste time in futile repining. Upon his dismissal two years earlier he had, in spite of his advanced years, given no thought to retiring. On the contrary, he had promptly embarked on a series of new activities that, as one friend stated, would have taxed the energies of many men half his age.

One of the first of these was the opening of an office as a consulting engineer in downtown San Francisco. There, during the next few years, he received a variety of commissions to investigate and report on the feasibility of numerous irrigation projects and land companies then being organized in the Sacramento and San Joaquin valleys. At the conclusion of one of the first of these assignments, his report, consisting of forty-eight pages and illustrated by maps and diagrams, was issued in pamphlet form in 1896, addressed to "The Landowners of Reclamation District No. 108," an organization then in process of development in the vicinity of Knight's Valley.

Besides maintaining his engineering office he took up his duties as professor of geography at the University of California at Berkeley, crossing the bay three times each week to lecture before his classes there. Moreover, he continued to maintain his observatory in Lafayette Square, conducting astronomical observations there that frequently kept him up half the night for weeks on end; and in addition, he somehow found time to contribute a long series of articles on scientific subjects to a San Francisco newspaper, the *Examiner*. Finally, he plunged with renewed energy into his researches and writing on the routes followed by the first navigators to visit the Northwest Coast.

All these projects Davidson during the next half-dozen years pursued with undiminished industry, spurred on by the knowledge that the time for accomplishing them was growing short. In that connection he, in 1900, being then in his seventy-fifth year, wrote to an old-time Philadelphia friend, Franklin S. Edmonds: "I have so much laid out to do and so few years in which to do it!" In his determination to put to productive use such additional time as might be allotted him, he, besides carrying on the numerous tasks already enumerated, conducted a voluminous correspondence with fellow scientists in the field of geodesy and astronomy, served as president of the Geographical Society of the Pacific and as corresponding member of other learned societies, and continued frequently to address public meetings on subjects on which he had come to be recognized as an outstanding authority. All in all, as a writer for one of the San Francisco papers pointed out after his death, he led a notably full and active life for one of his years.

XVII · teacher and writer

Davidson's first connection with the University of California, with which he was to be closely identified for nearly four decades, began on November 2, 1870, when the Board of Regents appointed him nonresident professor of geodesy and astronomy. In a summary of his activities written in the late 1880's he states that the noted astronomer Professor Benjamin Peirce, then superintendent of the Coast Survey, warmly approved of his taking the post, which, however, entailed no salary since a rule of the Survey forbade its members from accepting compensation from other sources.

Just how much time he gave to his teaching duties at Berkeley in the next few years is not definitely known today. It is likely, however, that it was limited to occasional lectures; for throughout that period he was frequently absent from his San Francisco headquarters on field trips to stations up and down the coast, and on special assignments to more distant points. It is of record that in the spring of 1874 he gave a course, intended primarily for engineering students, dealing with the functions and purposes of the Coast Survey. In it he outlined the methods employed by the bureau in carrying out its task of charting the nation's coastlines and aiding navigators by accurately fixing the positions of headlands, harbors, and so forth, locating and marking reefs, shoals, and similar hazards, and collecting data on weather conditions and the characteristics of ocean currents.

In 1877 a new phase of his association with the University began when Governor William Irwin appointed him to the Board of Regents to fill a vacancy caused by the death of John B. Felton. Davidson continued to serve on the board until Felton's term expired in March, 1884. During part of that period he was a member of a committee charged with making a survey of the University's activities and of suggesting means by which its usefulness to the state and the nation might be enhanced. One of the commitee's recommendations—which almost certainly originated with Davidson—was that the state legislature be asked to appropriate $10,000 "for an observatory and the mounting of a telescope for observations on the physical character of the heavenly bodies, together with magnetic, earthquake and meteorological observations." This project was eventually realized, though on a far larger scale than originally proposed, when, in accordance with James Lick's will, title to the great observatory on Mount Hamilton was formally transferred to the University on the observatory's completion in 1888.

Finally, on July 1, 1898, some three years after his dismissal from the Survey, Davidson, while holding his position as nonresident professor of geodesy and astronomy, received a second appointment, this time with the title of professor of geography. For the next seven years he was an active member of the faculty. Although he was seventy-three when he accepted this post and was, as his associate, Professor Ruliff S. Holway, wrote in 1912, "eight years beyond the limit usually fixed for the retirement of college professors," he entered on his new duties with characteristic enthusiasm and energy. Thereafter until 1905 his tall, erect figure, flowing white beard, and genial smile, crowned by a broad-brimmed black felt hat, became a familiar sight as on his triweekly visits he strode across the campus on his way to and from his office in the Mechanics Building.

During part of that time he headed the newly organized Department of Commerce, the forerunner of the present Department of Business Administration. Recalling this period, his daughter Ellinor wrote years later that he "lectured only," leaving administrative and other work in connection with his department to others, and adding that his lectures were attended "by large classes of seniors." She stated that one—but by no means the only—reason for the popularity of his courses was the fact that, because of his wide acquaintance with leaders in business and engineering circles all over the coast, he was frequently able to find jobs for students who wished to enter these fields. "As Professor of Geography at the University of California," wrote J. J. Gilbert in the *Bulletin* of the American Geographical Society for January, 1912, "his profound knowledge and his faculty for imparting information, and his genial way with students, made his class one of the most popular in the university."

One of his students was Joseph N. LeConte, son of the eminent geologist, and himself later head of the Engineering Department at the University. In 1946 the younger LeConte recalled an early meeting with Davidson in these words:

Several of us students were then [in the spring of 1890] planning a pack-trip through the then almost unexplored region of the high Sierra about the headwaters of the Kings and Kern Rivers. Professor Davidson was greatly interested and anxious that we do some original triangulation in this wild region, for, he said, many of the great peaks of this part of the Sierra were very incorrectly placed on existing maps. So he lent us a light mountain transit with diagonal eyepiece so we could observe the sun and get material for determining latitude, difference in longitude, time and azimuth. He also wrote out for us complete directions for working up our observations. We were surprised that he trusted us with these valuable instruments. However, we did as directed and obtained many good readings on some of the main crest peaks, including Mt. Gould and Mt. Whitney.

LeConte recalled, too, that when Davidson became professor of geography in 1898, "He was given an office in the Mechanics Building right next to mine. I saw a great deal of him—used to attend his lectures frequently, and sometimes operated the electric stereopticon for him." Another old acquaintance, Alexander McAdie, once stated that "two or three times a week" Davidson crossed the bay to Berkeley from his home in San Francisco and, after his morning lecture, "about eight of the professors would gather in Professor Armes' room at the [Faculty] Club" for lunch and prolonged discussion, during which they were, in McAdie's words, "all boys together."

In 1905, however, the old man's eyesight, which had been failing for some time, became so dim that, on June 30, he retired from active teaching, becoming professor emeritus. Two years later, in the fall of 1907, an operation having partially restored his vision, he voluntarily resumed his lectures, though on a much less frequent schedule. His last official appearance at the university was in 1910 when he was honored by having the degree of LL.D. conferred on him by President Benjamin Ide Wheeler.

All through the period of his active teaching career, Davidson continued his researches into the routes and landing places of the navigators who had first explored the Northwest Coast, a project on which he had been intermittently engaged for many years. His interest in this subject had come about naturally, as we have seen, for at the time of his arrival on the coast in 1850, the only existing charts of much of the shoreline were those made by the early visitors, and he had sought out and familiarized himself with as many of these documents as he could locate. Moreover, it was not long until his study of the maps and narratives stirred in him a deep and abiding curiosity and a determination to uncover all that could be learned about them and their voyages. His enthusiasm for this research grew with the years, so that during the final period of his life this study absorbed a major part of his time and, in the words of one acquaintance, "became a sort of obsession with him."

Thus all through the late 1890's and early 1900's he continued his researches and wrote voluminously about the early navigators and their explorations, scarcely a year passing without the publication of some paper bearing on one phase or another of his central theme. These ranged from brief digests of lectures before historical or geographical societies, and occasional contributions to magazines, to substantial, fully documented volumes hundreds of pages in length. Moreover, because of Davidson's long study of original sources, plus his intimate, firsthand knowledge of virtually every mile of the extended coastline, these historical-geographical writings had a degree of authenticity that everywhere commanded respect. Long before his death in 1911 he had come to be generally recognized as the foremost authority on the subject.

That his interest in this field was a long-standing one is clear from the fact that as early as 1855 he was industriously collecting material pertaining to it. Thus we find him, in a postscript to a letter to Superintendent Bache in January of that year, stating triumphantly that he had just ordered a set of Vancouver's *Voyage of Discovery to the North Pacific Ocean and round the World,* from a London bookseller. His first extended writing on the subject appeared, as stated earlier, in the first (1858) printing of his *Directory for the Pacific Coast of the United States.* This, however, was only the beginning, for as his researches continued he steadily accumulated additional data, and these were incorporated in much amplified form in the three editions of the directory that followed—in 1862, 1869, and 1889—the last two of which were called the "Coast Pilot."

Although in the strictest sense such historical material had no logical place in the "Coast Pilots"—these works being primarily designed as practical guides to mariners whose ships plied the coastal waters—yet time has proved that these sections had a far greater permanent value than all the rest. For although the bulk of the data on navigation has, of course, long since become outdated, the wealth of historical information they contain—much of it unavailable elsewhere—has made the successive editions of the work, particularly that of 1889, highly useful alike to scholars and general readers interested in that field of early exploration.

Davidson's writings on the pioneer navigators of the west coast appeared not only in the successive editions of the "Coast Pilot" but in the annual *Reports* of the superintendent of the Survey. Thus the *Report* for the year 1885 contains as one of its appendixes a nine-page "Collection of Some Magnetic Variations off the Coast of California and Mexico, Observed by Spanish Navigators in the Last Quarter of the Eighteenth Century." That for the following year had a more ambitious work, this one occupying a full hundred pages, entitled "An Examination of Some of the Early Voyages of Discovery and Exploration on the Northwest Coast of America from 1539 to 1603," a project that, as Davidson stated at the time, had occupied most of such time as he could spare from his regular duties for two full years.

The list of early navigators who touched on the coast and whose charts and narratives he indefatigably searched out is a long one, including as it does Cabrillo (1542), Cermeño (1595), Vizcaíno (1602), and numerous other early Spanish and Portuguese explorers, together with Drake (1579) and such later visitors as Vancouver (1792), Cook (1778), the Russians, Bering and Chirikov (1741), on down to Kotzebue (1816), Beechey (1826), Duhaut-Cilly (1827), Wilkes (1842), and a host of others.

Of particular interest to him were the explorations conducted in the first half of the eighteenth century by Vitus Jonassen Bering and Alexei Ilich Chirikov, whose (in Davidson's words)

"almost superhuman effort" in exploring the far-northern waters
and coastlines he recorded in "The Tracks and Landfalls of
Bering and Chirikov on the Northwest Coast of America," published in 1901.

The major share of his historical writings, however, related to
the great English explorer and freebooter, Francis Drake, and
in particular to attempts to fix definitely the spot where, in June,
1579, Drake had made his historic landing on the northern California coast. To that involved and much-debated problem Davidson applied himself with characteristic thoroughness and gusto.
For the controversy—which, incidentally, has continued down to
the present day—was a particularly lively one half a century
ago, with some authorities contending that Drake had sailed his
Golden Hinde through the Golden Gate and beached her on the
shores of San Francisco Bay, others just as positively maintaining
that he had landed in the cove some distance farther up the coast
now known as Drake's Bay, and still others holding that Bodega
Bay was his landing place.

Davidson, who in the beginning allied himself with the first
group, later swung over to the other side and became the most
ardent advocate of the Drake's Bay theory. After years of careful
study of the charts and narratives of members of Drake's party
and of other early explorers of the coast—during which, he once
stated, he had "obtained copies of manuscripts from the British
Museum, from Madrid, and elsewhere"—and drawing on his
intimate knowledge of the topography, winds, and currents of
the area, he in 1908 published his final conclusions. These were
contained in a work bearing the formidable title "Francis Drake
on the Northwest Coast of America in the Year 1579. The Golden
Hinde Did Not Anchor in the Bay of San Francisco," which appeared first in the *Transactions and Proceedings* of the Geographical Society of the Pacific (Series II, Vol. V, 1908) and
later that year was issued as a separate volume.

His identification of Drake's Bay as the explorer's stopping place, although it was supported by much careful reasoning and all the documentary evidence then available, nonetheless failed to convince historians who held different views. The consequence was that the argument went merrily on both during Davidson's lifetime and later. A letter in the files of the American Geographical Society in New York throws an amusing side light on his efforts to win distinguished converts to his theory. On January 16, 1892, he wrote George C. Hurlbert of the society, as follows: "When your friend Edward Everett Hale was out here I arranged with Captain Hooker (U. S. Customs) to take him to Drake's Bay, and with the proprietor, Charles Webb Howard, of the ranch [which occupied the land bordering on the cove] to show him the anchorage—approaching it from the northwest, etc., and then take him over the country; but the religious people had him in tow and he gave up what he had written me from San Diego was 'one of the objects of my life.'. . ."

Among the authorities who disagreed with Davidson's conclusions was Henry R. Wagner, whose writings, including the *Spanish Voyages to the Northwest Coast of America in the Sixteenth Century,* published in 1939, likewise go into the question in detail and make use of certain documentary evidence not available to Davidson. Wagner, however, although differing with his predecessor's findings, gives him credit (in the *California Historical Society Quarterly* for December, 1932) in these words: "The mere fact that he may have been mistaken in some of his historical deductions drawn from inconclusive sources can in no wise detract from the practical results which he achieved in the interests of science and to the benefit of his adopted state." Wagner then goes on to state that: "In many respects he was the most remarkable man that has ever lived in California, and all of us who live in California and enjoy the fruits of his labor should honor his memory."

When, in 1936, interest in the long-drawn-out controversy was rekindled by the discovery of what, to many experts, appeared to be the identical metal plate Drake had caused to be placed "upon a faire great poste" near his anchorage more than three and a half centuries earlier, there were many who regretted that Davidson had not lived long enough to examine it. Few doubted that his verdict on the authenticity of the celebrated "plate of brasse" would in due time have been given, or that his opinion when rendered would have been backed by characteristically sound and logical reasoning.

XVIII · last years

By the end of the century Davidson had come to be widely regarded as the dean of western scientists, the man to whom the public looked for enlightenment on subjects having to do with any of the fields of science in which he had made himself an authority. This was a role he willingly accepted, for he had always been a teacher at heart, and he liked nothing better than to share his highly specialized knowledge with interested laymen. Thus, as stated earlier, he for years welcomed groups of students and others to his Lafayette Square observatory, and in later life did much to promote a wider understanding and appreciation of the advances of science on the part of the general public, by his frequent lectures and by numerous articles in west coast magazines and newspapers.

From the outset of his career on the coast he was always generous in putting the results of his work with the Survey at the disposal of writers for the San Francisco journals, who frequently consulted and quoted him on topics having to do with his specialties. Thus the *Morning Call*, in an editorial tribute published at the time of his death, stated: "Among newspapermen he was an especial favorite ... always ready to explain difficult scientific problems. Always liberal of his knowledge ... his house on the hill was the resort of those wanting information on topics of scientific interest. . . ."

Not only was he for many years a main reliance of the San Francisco journalists seeking comment or elucidation on such subjects currently in the news, but he himself was a not infrequent contributor to the columns of their papers. In the earlier period, most of such writing as he did appeared in the *Alta California*, the owner of which, Fred McCrellish, was a close friend. It was in the *Alta* that much of the material on the navigational hazards of the coast, later incorporated in the "Coast Pilot of California, Oregon, and Washington," was first published. Later, other San Francisco dailies—the *Bulletin,* the *Chronicle,* and the *Examiner*—together with the *Overland Monthly,* the *Californian,* and a number of other weekly and monthly magazines of the area, from time to time published his writings.

These were all casual contributions, written, like his more serious papers for scientific publications, at such times as he could spare from his official duties. Some years after his retirement from the Coast Survey, however, he took up newspaper writing in earnest, and from the early 1900's until only a few weeks before his death he contributed an extensive series of articles to the San Francisco *Examiner,* many of which were printed on its editorial page. These papers covered a wide variety of subjects, ranging from comment on scientific matters then in the news to sketches of the first explorers of the coast, reminiscences of his early work with the Survey, discussions of the origin and meaning of western place names, and numerous more or less related topics.

One subject to which he often returned was the desirability of supplying further information and navigational aids to the masters of ships plying Pacific Coast waters, and in particular to the need for a thorough hydrographic survey of the area and a study of the offshore ocean currents. In that connection he wrote in one of his papers: "The government should at once provide the means for a systematic survey of the currents of the North Pacific and should begin the work along our own coast and proceed with reasonable rapidity . . . assigning at least two vessels to that work."

Some light on his connection with the *Examiner* is revealed by a brief exchange of letters which took place in 1904. That enterprising paper, having sponsored a project to erect an observatory on Mount Tamalpais to sight and report on incoming ships, engaged Davidson to select a site and design the little building. For this service the newspaper paid him a fee of $100. When, however, he declined payment for an article he had written in support of the undertaking, one of the *Examiner* reporters, Henry Bigelow, remonstrated at his lack of business acumen. Davidson replied, stating that their mutual friend Louis Sloss, head of the Alaska Commercial Company, "will call me a d—— fool" for refusing to accept the paper's check. To this, T. T. Williams, the *Examiner*'s business manager, replied succinctly: "Sloss is right!"

It was not until Davidson neared his eightieth birthday that he at last was compelled to curtail his activities. The reason then was not a decline in his mental alertness but a growing physical handicap, his failing eyesight. This affliction evidently did not reach serious proportions until early in 1905. Once started, however, its progress was so rapid that by June of that year his vision was so impaired that he was forced to give up his thrice-weekly trips to Berkeley, and he accordingly tendered his resignation as professor of geography at the university. But even when he was so nearly blind that, in the words of Professor Ruliff S. Holway (who had taken over his classes), "he was able to read only through a narrow slit in a blackened cardboard under favorable light and with the help of the strongest glasses," he grimly continued his researches into the voyages of the early explorers.

Working under difficulties that would have discouraged less resolute scholars, he wrote steadily, not only continuing his occasional brief pieces for the *Examiner* but industriously pushing ahead on more ambitious projects. Thus, in 1908, he completed and published his authoritative, fully documented book on Drake, and followed it two years later with a comprehensive paper on "The Origin and the Meaning of the Name California," which was published first in the *Transactions and Proceedings* of the Geographical Society of the Pacific (Series II, Vol. VI, Part 1). These were both works based on long and painstaking examination of original sources, including not only the widely scattered maps and charts of the navigators but their written chronicles, some published, others in manuscript.

An indication of the handicaps under which he carried forward these works may be gained by a reading of a group of letters written by him from his home in San Francisco to Porter Garnett, then a member of the staff of the Bancroft Library on the Berkeley campus. The appearance of the letters themselves makes it clear that their writer's sight was all but gone. Sometimes there was no ink in his pen, and the words are dim and unreadable; the lines slant at different angles and frequently run together, and often the pages themselves are upside down, with the printed letterhead at the bottom. These curious communications all contain requests that Garnett consult certain books, maps, or manuscripts in the Library's collection in order to supply needed data, verify citations, and the like. One, dated September 4, 1908, begins: "I am so nearly blind that I cannot hunt up authorities, so will you . . ." Another, on June 8, 1909, states: "I have not been able to read since last October . . ."

On May 9, 1909—his eighty-fourth birthday—he submitted to a second operation, this time for the removal of cataracts from both eyes. At first it was thought that this had been successful and that his normal vision would be restored. In its story of the operation the *Examiner* stated that the venerable scientist's blindness had been "swept away in time for him to see Halley's Comet," which was due to make its next appearance the following year. But although the sight of one eye was partially restored, the complete cure he had hoped for failed to materialize, and on October 23, 1911, he wrote Captain J. J. Gilbert, of the Coast and Geodetic Survey in Washington, that "the left eye is nearly blind and the right not much better." This same letter, written only a few weeks before his death, records that in the previous July he had suffered a bad fall and had been confined to his bed for a full month, "longer than at any time since I was born."

Yet, in spite of his continuing semiblindness and a growing physical feebleness, the indomitable old scholar continued his historical researches, not only on the subjects that had long interested him but in new fields. Thus, in the last of his letters to the Survey's headquarters at Washington, he requests that copies of two government publications be sent him, explaining that "they relate to [John C.] Fremont's claims"—a highly controversial subject on which he was then informing himself. This was written on November 10, 1911, a scant three weeks before his death.

In the meantime, his growing infirmities had little by little forced him to abandon the active life he had lived for so many years. His extensive travels in connection with his work for the Survey—during which, he once stated, he had covered 393,720 miles on official business, "always with instruments, note-books and sketch-book in hand"—had, of course, become a thing of the past. As his eyesight grew weaker, his appearances in public first were curtailed and then ceased entirely, as did also his attendance at the meetings of the local scientific societies with which he had been so long associated. In the last few months he rarely left the big frame house on Washington Street where he had lived for nearly a quarter century. During all this time, however, he daily spent hours at his desk in the second-floor study while he tenaciously continued his writings and conducted an active correspondence with fellow astronomers, geographers, and historians in various parts of the world.

Visitors privileged to enter that sanctum found it curiously like a museum, its walls and much of the floor space crowded with objects accumulated during a lifetime of travel to remote places: baskets and implements of the Indians of California, the Northwest, and Alaska; examples of Eskimo arts and crafts; souvenirs picked up in Japan, India, and other Far Eastern countries; scientific instruments, medals and diplomas attesting to his membership in scientific societies in many lands, and much else. As one commentator truly wrote after Davidson's death, he had "lived his last years surrounded by the mementoes of more than sixty years of productive work in the far corners of the world."

XIX · personal qualities

Davidson was, as a friend once commented, a man who, wherever he might be encountered, carried in his appearance and bearing unmistakable evidences of the outdoors. Throughout his life he was physically active and, as he often stated, was far happier roughing it with his surveying parties in the field than performing routine administrative work. All who knew him agreed that his energy and physical stamina were prodigious. Of well above average height and strongly built, he had the bearing and manner of an athlete, his figure being erect and his movements brisk and assured even in old age. Until he was well past sixty he liked nothing better than to set forth on astronomical or triangulation expeditions—usually into remote and rugged mountain areas—where he conducted himself with a tireless energy that frequently taxed the strength and endurance of younger companions.

His temperament in many respects was on a par with his

physical prowess. He was a man of decided opinions, tenaciously held, and although he was ever ready to listen attentively to the arguments of those who disagreed with his conclusions, his decisions, once made, were rarely reversed. Yet although there was clearly a vein of stubbornness in his nature, and although, in his work for the Survey, he demanded prompt obedience on the part of his subordinates, this was combined with a warmth and affability that won the regard and respect even of those who differed with him. Of this phase of his character, Ruliff S. Holway wrote in 1912: "Simple and unassuming in appearance, he bore the mark of one accustomed to command, and possessed a strong and dominating personality. The men who served under him learned at once to obey unquestioningly his slightest order, yet his warm-hearted and generous nature caused them to be strongly attached to him."

Thus, although Davidson had a well-merited reputation as a disciplinarian, it was observed that all during his years with the Coast Survey he bore a full share of the hardships and dangers of life in the field, putting in longer hours than any of the others and, when something particularly hazardous needed to be done, undertaking the task himself. Moreover, in his reports to headquarters at Washington, he rarely failed to give full credit to his associates whenever a particularly exacting or difficult mission had been performed. Thus, in 1852, in writing of the difficulties encountered while his party was operating in the vicinity of Cape Flattery, he stated: "The topography has been executed at the risk of the life of every one at work on it," and went on to point out the dangers involved whenever the group was obliged to make landings through the surf in their heavily laden small boats—a feat which, as he stated elsewhere, he and his companions had accomplished "more than forty times."

Not only the hazards of such landings and of working in remote and rugged areas but hostile Indians frequently constituted a real source of danger. During the early part of 1857, while he

and his party were mapping the Puget Sound shoreline, his
letters to Bache made frequent reference to these matters and
clearly reveal his concern for the safety of those in his charge.
Thus, on January 19, while preparing to set out to the north
from San Francisco, he wrote: "Can you obtain authority for
me to get 1000 rifle cartridges from the army here? I should
feel more satisfied with some on board." On May 7 of the same
year, he added: "In the present state of Indian affairs in Washington Territory I would urge upon your attention the necessity
of supplying the brig with two small cannon, say 6-pounders,"
and stated that he had "exhausted every method of obtaining
means of defense" from military and naval authorities on the
coast.

Something of the rigors of the work in the mountainous country of California's northern coast is reflected in another letter to
Bache, this one written near the end of 1859 and outlining his
plans for the next few months.

I shall [he reported] occupy Ross Mountain this winter and try to
bring the secondary and tertiary work from Tomales to that place.
During that time I shall endeavor to get ten or fifteen horses or mules,
equip an armed party of about five men carrying nothing but provisions
and arms, and penetrate the mountains to the northward.... At each
selected station we shall erect one or two log cabins for the heliotropers
and the future triangulation points; erect signals that will require the
carrying of large iron signal bolts, blocks, tackles, paint, etc., and study
the most feasible methods and routes of conveying instruments and provisions and party.... No roads exist, no trails, inhabitants are very
few; no bridges to cross the torrents in the wet season....

The work cannot be advanced in winter; reconnaissance must be
made in the spring when the grass will feed the animals; hunters must
be allowed the party to supply game; all tents, equipment, books and
instruments not absolutely necessary must be abandoned; no provisions
or cooking utensils but what are absolutely necessary can be taken; pro-
tection against straggling bands of hostile Indians must be efficient; all
moving must be done with pack animals....

In view of the hardships and exertions involved in such work, it is not surprising that Davidson, despite his physical strength, often overtaxed himself to the injury of his health. Both his letters of the period and the diary he kept intermittently during these years make frequent references to illnesses. Some were recurring attacks of the Panama fever he had contracted while preparing to make a survey for a ship canal across the Isthmus of Darien. What he, along with others of the Survey's field parties, chiefly suffered from, however, was rheumatism, the result of prolonged exposure to the elements in all kinds of weather. All through his first years in the West he was periodically seized with such attacks, some so severe that they forced him to leave his field parties and seek medical aid in San Francisco.

It was no doubt largely as a result of such illnesses that Davidson during the early part of his stay on the coast often expressed dissatisfaction with the conditions prevailing there. A lack of sufficient funds or adequate equipment to carry on the Survey's work was another frequent source of complaint, as was also the smallness of the pay he and his associates received as compared with the lavish wage scales then prevailing on the coast. Intrigues and jealousies between parties engaged in different phases of the work were an added reason for discontent. As early as December, 1851, he wrote to Superintendent Bache from Ewing Harbor: "I wish to state distinctly that it is not for love of the coast that I offer to stay, for it presents embarrassments and difficulties not to be found on the Atlantic. . . . In the one and two-thirds years my expenses have eaten up all my per diem and six months pay; so heavy have they been that I have made up my mind to leave the Survey at the expiration of the time for which I volunteered. . . ."

So frequent did these complaints become that Bache, whose letters were usually full of encouragement and kindly advice to his young aide, was constrained to admonish him in these words:

"You have so many first rate qualities, that I always feel cha-
grined when I think you give way to the tendency to look on the
gloomy side. . . . I do hope you will change the tone of your
letters." Evidently Davidson heeded this advice, for his chief's
subsequent communications contain no further references to the
matter. Moreover, as time passed and Davidson grew more familiar with conditions on the frontier—meanwhile receiving increas-
ingly more important assignments with the Survey—his critical
attitude gradually disappeared, and, as we have seen, he presently reached the decision to settle there permanently. After the
Civil War years, which he had spent on the Atlantic Coast, he
welcomed the opportunity to return to California, and thereafter
as long as he lived he looked on himself as a Far Westerner—
which indeed he was—and was so regarded by friends and acquaintances everywhere.

That his presence on the coast throughout most of the turbulent
1850's, involving as it did his close association with the hetero-
geneous groups characteristic of frontier society, exerted a
marked and lasting influence on his habits and point of view
is obvious to those familiar with his career. Because, throughout
the early years, means of communicating with Washington were
so slow and unreliable, he frequently found it necessary to rely
on his own judgment in planning and carrying out the Survey's work on the Pacific Coast, he learned to shoulder responsibilities and develop qualities of leadership far sooner than he
would have under other circumstances.

One permanent—and amusing—result of his early experiences on the west coast was that, probably because of his being
placed in charge of the rough crews of the *Fauntleroy* and other
Survey ships, he acquired so varied and fluent a command of
profanity that for years thereafter his casual conversations were
often studded with forceful words and phrases not usually heard
in the polite circles of his day. In that connection, a Berkeley
friend, J. N. Bowman, recalled that Davidson once professed to

him that he "did not feel really at ease with anyone unless he could swear in his company." Bowman added that, although the scientist's conversations were likely to be generously larded with oaths, he had the faculty of using them without giving the impression that he was swearing. Alexander McAdie once stated, however, that when Davidson, at the age of seventy-three, was appointed professor of geography at the University of California, he to a great extent succeeded in breaking himself of that long-standing frontier habit.

XX · a summing up

The breadth of Davidson's interests, no less than his abundant energy, is attested by the important part he came to play in the activities of virtually every scientific and scholarly organization functioning in California in the final third of the last century.

His long and close association with one of these bodies, the California Academy of Sciences, has already been mentioned. Not only did he serve continuously as the Academy's president from 1871 to 1886, but throughout that entire period he took an uncommonly active part in its affairs. In later life he recalled that within one period of nine years he presented seventy-three papers before members and their guests, besides presiding at numerous other meetings and introducing guest speakers, most of whom he himself had invited to appear.

Another scientific institution with which he was long closely identified was the Geographical Society of the Pacific. Davidson indeed was from the beginning the leading spirit in its activities. He was one of the original group that brought about its organization on March 18, 1881; he became its president on August 2 of that year and continued to occupy that post without a break until his death three decades later. During its early years the society maintained an office and meeting room at 217 Powell Street, later moving to more commodious quarters at 475 California Street. There it remained until the fire of 1906, in which holocaust its extensive library—including, it is said, many of Davidson's early writings and later papers—was consumed.

In the last thirty years of his life a great many of his writings on geographical and historical subjects appeared under the imprint of the Geographical Society, either in its *Transactions and Proceedings* or as separate publications. These, to name but a few, included "The Tracks and Landfalls of Bering and Chirikof," first read before the members in 1898 and later published in extended form in the society's *Transactions and Proceedings*, as were also "The Discovery of San Francisco Bay" (1907), "The Glaciers of Alaska . . . Shown on Russian Charts . . ." (1904), his much-debated "Francis Drake on the Northwest Coast of America" (1908), and, in his eighty-fifth year, his authoritative 50-page paper on "The Origin and Meaning of the Name California."

These, however, were by no means the only western scientific groups with which he was affiliated. He was made an honorary member of the San Francisco Microscopical Society on its founding in 1881 and was long a faithful attendant at its meetings, frequently in the role of speaker. He was one of a group that, in 1886, reactivated the long-dormant California Historical Society, and he subsequently served several terms as its vice-president. And when the prominent western mountaineering society, the Sierra Club, was founded in 1892, he was one of its charter members, and for many years served on its board of directors.

One of his associates on the Sierra Club board was John Muir, the eminent naturalist, explorer, and writer. The two men had, of course, a great deal in common, both having penetrated into many of the more remote and picturesque areas of the Pacific Coast, including Alaska, and written much of their travels. Years later, Professor Joseph N. LeConte, himself an ardent mountaineer, recalled that at the Sierra Club directors' meetings the two would sometimes fall into reminiscences of their experiences on the Alaska mainland and in the Aleutians. LeConte added that these prolonged discussions frequently proved so fascinating to the others that the purposes for which the board had assembled were completely forgotten and the meetings adjourned without transacting any business at all.

Davidson's affiliations with such groups were, however, not confined to those of the Pacific Coast. As early as 1853 he was made a life member of the Academy of Natural Sciences at Philadelphia. In 1866 he became a member of the American Philosophical Society of that city and eight years later was elected to the National Academy of Sciences at Washington.

Thereafter, as his professional reputation continued to grow, the list of scientific bodies in which he held membership lengthened year by year. Thus in 1881 he was elected a fellow of the American Association for the Advancement of Science, in 1887 an associate fellow of the American Academy of Arts and Sciences of Boston, and two years later a charter member of the National Geographic Society. In that same year, 1889, he was made a corresponding member of the American Geographical Society of New York. In the meantime, recognition of his contributions in the fields of geodesy and astronomy had come to be recognized farther afield, and in 1888 he was made an honorary corresponding member of the Royal Scottish Geographical Society at Edinburgh, and a year later of the Royal Geographical Society at London. Finally, in 1897, he was elected an honorary member of the American Society of Civil Engineers.

Besides those listed above, a variety of other honors were bestowed on him, including these honorary academic degrees: Doctor of Philosophy by Santa Clara College in 1876; of Doctor of Science by the University of Pennsylvania in 1889; and Doctor of Laws by the University of California in 1910. In addition, he was made a foreign corresponding member of the Bureau of Longitudes of France in 1894 and, in the same year, honorary vice-president of the Geographic Congress in London. To these honors were soon added memberships in the Academy of Sciences of the French Institute, the Swedish Anthropological and Geographical Society, and the Geographical Association of Berlin. At the time of his death he held memberships in more than forty scientific and learned societies in this country and abroad.

Two further distinctions were conferred on him near the end of his life. In 1907 the Norwegian government made him a member of the Order of Saint Olaf in recognition of his contributions to scientific knowledge; and a year later the American Geographical Society awarded him the Charles P. Daly medal.

In connection with this Daly award it should be noted that Davidson's last surviving child, his daughter Ellinor, on her death in the mid-1940's, bequeathed the sum of $5,000 to the American Geographical Society to provide a gold medal and research fund in her father's memory. Her will directed that the Davidson Medal be bestowed by the Society "for exceptional achievement in research or exploration in the Pacific Ocean or the lands bordering thereon," and that the fund be used "to promote research in surveying and mapping" in the same area. The medal, designed by the eminent sculptor Paul Manship, has on one side a bas-relief profile of Davidson, surrounded by the words "American Geographical Society" and "The George Davidson Medal"; and on the reverse, "For Research in the Pacific Area" and the name of the recipient. In 1952 the first Davidson Medal was conferred on George B. Cressey.

Because Davidson throughout his adult life had been a student as well as a man of action, he early became an avid collector of books, particularly in fields related to his professional interests.

From time to time, the diary he kept intermittently during most of his career, and also his letters to friends and associates, record his pleasure at having located and acquired some work for which he had long been searching. These books grew so numerous that in his later years visitors to the Washington Street house found them not only lining the walls of the library and second-floor study but overflowing into other rooms and even stacked in the halls and on the stairway.

Spurred by his deep and abiding interest in the history of the early exploration of the coast, he accumulated an outstanding collection of narratives by and about the pioneer navigators of the region, many of them ordered from the catalogs of rare book dealers in this country and in Europe and others picked up in the course of his periodical trips to the east coast and abroad.

The extent of his collection in that field at length became so well known to local scholars that when Robert Louis Stevenson reached San Francisco in 1888 on his way to the South Seas, it was recommended to him as the local library most likely to contain material on a subject in which he was then deeply interested—the history and geography of the area he was about to visit. Whether the two men met has not been definitely established; it is known, however, that Stevenson, during his stay in San Francisco, borrowed and read several books from Davidson's library. Documentary evidence of this is contained in a letter pasted on the flyleaf of Volume I of a copy of a *Narrative of a Voyage round the World Performed in Her Majesty's Ship Sulphur during the Years 1836 to 1842* by Captain Sir Edward Belcher, R.N. (London, 1842). The letter, written on the stationery of the Occidental Hotel on Montgomery Street, reads:

San Francisco
Prof. Geo. Davidson   June 24, 1888
Dear Sir,

By the kindness of Mr. Yale I have received from you Krusenstern, Belcher and Langsdorff's voyages and Dalrymple's Historical Collection.

I cannot give the titles more fully as I have not yet been able to get on land, but I am truly grateful for this rich loan and will take all care that the works return to you in good condition.

Your obliged servant,

ROBERT LOUIS STEVENSON

Below is a note in Davidson's hand reading: "All returned on June 19, 1889 per Charles G. Yale."

Soon after Davidson's death in 1911, an effort was made to purchase several thousand of his scientific and historical books for the University of California Library. Nothing came of this project at the time; however, after the death of his daughter more than three decades later, by her bequest his extensive collection of books and papers went to two institutions with which he had been closely identified, part going to the University and part to the California Academy of Sciences.

Family ties were ever close to him, and his marriage to Ellinor Fauntleroy in October, 1858, marked the beginning of a happy domestic life that was to continue for many years. His bride, who was, as mentioned, a granddaughter of Robert Owen, the noted social reformer and founder of the celebrated scientific and cultural colony at New Harmony, Indiana, proved an ideal mate to one who during his entire adult life was engaged in scientific pursuits. Although she was retiring by nature and shunned anything that might bring her to public attention, she nonetheless was, according to their friends, deeply interested in his career and in unobtrusive ways was active in furthering it.

Throughout the earlier period of their stay on the west coast, Mrs. Davidson, as recounted earlier, often accompanied her husband on his field trips, sharing the discomforts of travel by the primitive facilities then available and the rough life in the isolated spots where astronomical and triangulation stations had been established. Later, when their three surviving children— two sons and a daughter—were old enough to travel, Davidson frequently took the entire family on the expeditions to foreign lands to which he had been assigned. Thus, in 1874–1875, they accompanied him on his mission to Japan and on round the world, and several years later, on his journey to Europe, where he was sent to examine the instruments of precision on display at the Paris Exposition of 1878.

From the early 1880's onward, visitors to the big, rambling Davidson house in San Francisco were impressed not only by the hospitality and graciousness of the hostess but by her grasp of the recondite scientific matters that were often under discussion there. By then the three children were growing up; the youngest was attending a local school, and the two sons, George and Thomas, were completing their education at Harvard.

Then, in 1900, came the first break in the closely knit family circle. The tragic death, by suicide, of thirty-eight-year-old George F. Davidson, whom Mary McAdie described as "remarkably clever and the pride of all our hearts," was a severe blow to his aging parents. The young man, who had been ill for some time and a patient in a sanatorium in the Napa Valley, was believed to have taken his life because he thought that he was losing his reason. Some six years later, Gertrude Atherton, on a visit to the Washington Street house, found the father still oppressed by the tragedy, which he believed to have been the result of faulty diagnosis of the young man's ailment by his physicians. "He told me," wrote she, "that George's sole trouble had been astigmatism and if the doctors had known enough to send him to an oculist he would never have imagined himself insane and killed himself." Thereafter the father, as long as he lived, yearly recorded in his diary the successive anniversaries of his son's death.

Mrs. Davidson, who had long been in frail health, died in 1907; and for the next four years the diminished household—the father and his two surviving children, Thomas and Ellinor, neither of whom ever married—continued to occupy the big frame house. The aged and all-but-blind scientist seldom ventured outdoors but resolutely continued his researches and writing on the voyages of the early navigators. This self-imposed task occupied him for many hours daily, in spite of the handicaps imposed by his failing vision and a growing physical feebleness.

On May 9, 1911, he passed his eighty-sixth birthday, and for another six months he maintained his usual schedule, working on the various projects he had under way, conducting an active correspondence with librarians and others in quest of information needed in his researches, contributing occasional articles to the San Francisco *Examiner,* and cheerfully greeting a succession of old friends who sought him out in his cluttered upstairs study. Then, late in November, he caught cold and took to his bed, and a week later, on the morning of December 2, 1911, died peacefully. Funeral services were held on December 4 at St. Mark's Episcopal Church in Berkeley, and were attended by what one journalist described as "one of the most notable groups of distinguished citizens ever assembled hereabouts," who had, he added, "come together in order to pay honor to the memory of the late, well-loved scientist."

· chronology

This outline of the important milestones in Davidson's career has been compiled, with certain additions and deletions, from two sources: a *Brief Memoranda of the Public Services of George Davidson, in Geodesy, Astronomy, etc.*, printed in pamphlet form in 1899, and a typewritten "Chronology of George Davidson," prepared by the U. S. Coast and Geodetic Survey at Washington, D.C., after Davidson's death in 1911.

1825 Born at Nottingham, England, May 9.

1832 Emigrated with parents to the United States; settled at Philadelphia.

1843–1844 Attended Central High School, Philadelphia; employed as magnetic observer and computer, Girard College Observatory.

1845 Entered U. S. Coast Survey as Clerk to Superintendent Alexander Bache.

1846 Was appointed Aide in U. S. Coast Survey; engaged in geodetic work; served as member of a field survey party in the Gulf of Mexico.

1847 Served as computer and observer; engaged in reconnaissance; took observations for latitude, etc.

1848 Made meteorological and astronomical observations; conducted triangulation work; received degree of A.M. from Central High School, Philadelphia.

1849 Engaged in triangulation and reconnaissance; made latitude and longitude observations, and reductions.

1850 Was assigned to duty on Pacific Coast; arrived at San Francisco, June 19.

1851–1852 Made latitude and longitude observations and lunar culminations; was in charge of topographical work and locating lighthouses.

1853–1856 Commanded Survey brig *R. H. Fauntleroy;* made astronomical and magnetic observations; surveyed Humboldt Bay; did triangulation work in southern California.

1857 Continued observations and surveys, mainly in Puget Sound area; appeared as witness in Limantour land grant case in San Francisco.

1858 Married Ellinor Fauntleroy, October 5; completed "Directory for the Pacific Coast of the United States."

1859 Directed main triangulation operations north of San Francisco; conducted latitude, azimuth, and magnetic observations.

1860 Continued main triangulation of California and observations listed above; returned to the Atlantic Coast.

1861 Carried on engineering duties in connection with defenses of Delaware River.

1862 Commanded Coast Survey steamer *Vixen* off Florida; made hydrographic surveys; compiled second edition of "Directory for the Pacific Coast of the United States."

1863 Served as assistant engineer, laying out and building fortifications for the defense of Philadelphia.

1864 Continued the work mentioned above; prepared report on lines of defense of the city.

1865 Went to Europe and brought home his ailing chief, Superintendent Bache.

1866 Conducted latitude, longitude, and azimuth observations; engaged in transatlantic longitude work, using newly laid Atlantic cable.

1867 Served as chief engineer of party exploring Isthmus of Darien for location of ship canal; headed party making geographical reconnaissance of Alaska; perfected Davidson Meridian Instrument.

1868 Was in charge of triangulation and astronomical work on Pacific Coast; began compilation of "Coast Pilot of Alaska."

1869 Led expedition to Alaska to observe total solar eclipse; published *Coast Pilot of Alaska* and third edition of *Coast Pilot of California, Oregon, and Washington Territory.*

1870 Engaged in astronomical work in southern California; was appointed Honorary Professor of Geodesy and Astronomy at University of California.

1871 Examined and reported on weights and balances at the U. S. Mint in San Francisco; was elected president of California Academy of Sciences.

1872 Conducted astronomical observations and reconnaissance in the High Sierra; surveyed California-Nevada boundary along the 120th meridian; became a member of the Annual Survey Commission, U. S. Mint, Philadelphia.

1873 Was appointed by President Grant one of three Commissioners of Irrigation of California; conferred with James Lick and announced Lick's intention to build world's largest telescope.

1874 Headed American transit-of-Venus expedition to Japan; conducted telegraphic longitude observations between Nagasaki, Vladivostok, and Tokyo.

1875 Traveled through China, India, Egypt, and Italy studying irrigation, reclamation methods, and harbor improvements; visited principal European observatories and makers of precision instruments.

1876 Observed the longest geodetic lines on record; made latitude, azimuth, and magnetic observations; received honorary degree of Ph.D. from Santa Clara College.

1877 Engaged in field, observatory, and administrative work; was appointed a Regent of University of California by Governor Irwin.

1878 Visited Paris Exposition to inspect instruments of precision in geodesy and astronomy; was appointed chairman of jury to judge moving powers of machinery displayed there.

1879 Observed longest geodetic lines (169 miles); founded and equipped Davidson Astronomical Observatory in Lafayette Square, San Francisco.

1880 Observed total solar eclipse from 6,000 feet in the Sierra; conducted extended observations for coefficient of refraction.

1881 Twice measured the Yolo base line; observed transit of Mercury; made spectroscopic observations; was one of the founders of the Geographical Society of the Pacific; was elected an honorary member of San Francisco Microscopical Society.

1882 Engaged in astronomical and geodetic work on Mount Tamalpais; made observations for geographical position of Lick Observatory; headed transit-of-Venus expedition to Cerro Roblero, New Mexico.

1883 Carried on field, office, and observatory duty; compiled field catalog of 1,278 time and circumpolar stars; examined Carson footprints.

1884 Continued field, office, and observatory duty; observed dark transits of Jupiter's satellites.

1885 Made annual assay of U. S. Mint at Philadelphia; began collection of magnetic data from old Spanish manuscripts.

1886 Made examination of assay, coin, and bullion weights at U. S. Mint in San Francisco; presented report to Board of Supervisors of San Francisco on city's sewerage system.

1887 Began complete revision of "Coast Pilot"; was made an Associate Fellow of the American Academy of Arts and Sciences.

1888 Made his first series of observations for variation of latitude; continued work on "Coast Pilot"; began research into landfalls of early navigators on northwest coast; was made an honorary corresponding member of the Royal Scottish Geographical Society.

1889 Measured Los Angeles base line three times; was appointed a delegate to meeting of the International Geodetic Association at Paris; was made a corresponding member of American Geographical Society; received honorary degree of Sc.D. from University of Pennsylvania.

1890 Made high-altitude astronomical observations in the Sierra; delivered an address on "The Discovery of Humboldt Bay, 1806"; was made an honorary corresponding member of Royal Geographical Society; appointed to Mississippi River Commission.

1891 Observed transit of Mercury; began second series of observations for variation of latitude, working six to nine hours nightly for fifteen months.

1892 Continued observations for variation of latitude and determined the period of variation by 6,768 results; engaged in field duty in main triangulation; was named president of board of engineers to devise sewerage system for San Francisco.

1893 Began third series of observations for variation of latitude; directed surveying of 405-mile California-Nevada boundary from Lake Tahoe to Colorado River; devised microscopic method of determining irregularities of micrometer screws.

1894 Presided at Geodetic Conference at Washington, D.C.; made telegraphic longitude observations in Washington, Oregon, and California; conducted fourth and fifth series of observations for variation of latitude; was made a foreign corresponding member of the Bureau of Longitude of France.

1895 Continued field, office, and observatory duty until June 30, when his connection with the U. S. Coast and Geodetic Survey was terminated.

1896 Opened office as consulting engineer in San Francisco; published paper on *The Genuineness of the "Jeannette" Relics; Some Evidences of Currents in the Polar Drift.*

1897 Inspected and rendered reports on irrigation and land projects in the Sacramento and San Joaquin valleys; elected an honorary member of American Society of Civil Engineers.

1898 Was appointed Professor of Geography at University of California; began writing "Tracks and Landfalls of Bering and Chirikof on the Northwest Coast of America . . . 1741"; was candidate for office of Superintendent of U. S. Coast and Geodetic Survey.

1899 Lectured three times weekly to students at the University of California; continued astronomical observations and researches into voyages of early explorers of west coast.

1900 Continued academic and observatory work; wrote "The Tracks and Landfalls of Bering and Chirikof on the Northwest Coast"; his son, George F. Davidson, died.

1901 Was elected a member of the Academy of Sciences of the Institute of France.

1902 Engaged in teaching, writing, and observatory work; lectured before various scientific societies and contributed to their publications.

1903 Published a 235-page treatise on *The Alaska Boundary,* a subject of controversy between the United States and England; made his findings available to members of the United States Commission appointed to arbitrate the dispute.

1904 Published *The Glaciers of Alaska That Are Shown on Russian Charts or Mentioned in Older Narratives;* continued lecturing before University of California classes; contributed brief articles on scientific and historical subjects to San Francisco *Examiner*.

1905 Eyesight began to fail; forced to abandon his astronomical work; resigned from the faculty of the University of California and became a professor emeritus.

1906 Made his Lafayette Square Observatory available to refugees rendered homeless by earthquake and fire of April 18; continued researches into location of Francis Drake's landing place on the California coast.

1907 Was created Knight of the Royal Order of Saint Olaf by King of Norway; published *The Discovery of San Francisco Bay*; Mrs. Davidson died.

1908 Was awarded Charles P. Daly medal by American Geographical Society; published his controversial *Francis Drake on the Northwest Coast of America in the Year 1579: The Golden Hinde Did Not Anchor in the Bay of San Francisco.*

1909 Wrote "The Origin and the Meaning of the Name California," published the following year.

1910 His eyesight partially restored by operation; received honorary degree of LL.D. from University of California.

1911 Died on December 2.

· published writings of george davidson

In the *Biennial Report* of the President of the University of California for the years 1896–1898 appeared a "List of the Published Writings of George Davidson," which contained some 135 items ranging from brief papers in newspapers, magazines, and scientific publications to bulky volumes hundreds of pages in length. These were arranged under six different headings: Geodesy, Astronomical, Instruments, Miscellaneous, Engineering, and Geography and Navigation. Four years later a *List and Catalogue of the Publications Issued by the U. S. Coast and Geodetic Survey: 1816–1902* was issued by the Government Printing Office; this lists numerous reports and other official communications written by Davidson and printed by the Survey during the half century he was connected with that bureau.

These, however, are a far from complete catalog of the products of his prolific pen in the course of his long career, for he continued to write industriously during the final years of his life, and numerous papers produced before 1898 were omitted from the list published that year.

The bibliography that follows, although it makes no claim to completeness, aims to include his more important writings in the fields in which he was primarily interested and in which he was a recognized authority: geodesy, astronomy, geography, and the history of early exploration on the Northwest Coast. Included, too—primarily to show the breadth of his scientific interests—are a number of papers contributed not only to the journals of the learned societies but to newspapers and magazines of general circulation.

Extracts from the Report of Assistant George Davidson . . . in Relation to the Work Executed . . . during the Past Year on the Coast of California and Oregon. *Report of the Superintendent of the Coast Survey, Showing Progress of the Survey during the Year 1852* (App. 17), pp. 101–103.

Observations Made on the Solar Eclipse at Humboldt Bay, California . . . *Report of the Superintendent of the Coast Survey . . . 1854* (App. 40, sec. 6), p. 127.

Extracts from a Descriptive Report . . . upon Localities on the Western Coast of the United States from the North Entrance of Rosario Strait, W.T., to the Southern Boundary of California. *Report of the Superintendent of the Coast Survey . . . 1855* (App. 26), pp. 176–185.

Directory for the Pacific Coast of the United States. *Report of the Superintendent of the Coast Survey . . . 1858* (App. 44), pp. 297–458. (Also issued separately.)

Directory for the Pacific Coast of the United States . . . [Revised edition.] *Report of the Superintendent of the Coast Survey . . . 1862* (App. 39), pp. 268–430. (Also issued separately.)

Report . . . Relative to the Resources and the Coast Features of Alaska Territory. *Report of the Superintendent of the Coast Survey . . . 1867* (App. 18), pp. 187–329.

Condensed Account of M. Hellert's Explorations on the Isthmus of Panama, Including His Special Explorations on the Isthmus of Darien; with Suggestions for Conducting a Future Survey. *Report of the Superintendent of the U. S. Coast Survey . . . 1868* (App. 15), pp. 260–277.

Report upon the Geographical Reconnaissance of the Coast of Alaska; the Physical Features and Prospective Resources of the Territory, and Proposed Aids to Navigation. 40th Cong., 2d sess. (1868), H. Ex. Doc. 177, pp. 219–360.

Scientific Expedition to Alaska. *Lippincott's Magazine,* II (November, 1868), 467–485.

Pacific Coast. Coast Pilot of Alaska (First Part), from Southern Boundary to Cook's Inlet. Washington: U. S. Coast Survey, 1869. 251 pp., 8 illus.

Pacific Coast. Coast Pilot of California, Oregon, and Washington Territory. Washington: U. S. Coast Survey, 1869. 262 pp., 33 illus.

Changes of Elevation and Azimuth Caused by the Action of the Sun, at Station Dominguez, California. *Report of the Superintendent of the U. S. Coast Survey . . . 1870* (App. 17), pp. 178–179.

Comparison of the Methods of Determining Heights by Means of Leveling, Verticle Angles and Barometric Measures from Observations at Bodega Head and Ross Mountain, Cal. *Report of the Superintendent of the U. S. Coast Survey . . . 1871* (App. 11), pp. 154–170.

Astronomical Observations on the Sierra Nevada. *Report of the Superintendent of the U. S. Coast Survey . . . 1872* (App. 9), pp. 173–176.

The Relative Value of Great and Small Altitudes for Astronomical Observations. *Proceedings of the California Academy of Sciences,* IV (Aug. 19, 1872), 251–252.

The Abrasions of the Continental Shores of N.W. America, and the Supposed Ancient Sea Levels. *Ibid.,* V (May 5, 1873), 90–97.

Field Catalogue of 983 Transit Stars; Mean Places for 1870.0. Washington: U. S. Coast and Geodetic Survey, 1874. 33 pp.

Mesh-Knot of the Tchin-cha-au Indians, Port Simpson, British Columbia. *Proceedings of the California Academy of Sciences,* V (1874), 400–401.

Report of the Board of Commissioners on the Irrigation of the San Joaquin, Tulare, and Sacramento Valleys of the State of California. 43d Cong., 1st sess. (1874), H. Ex. Doc. 290.

Note on the Probable Cause of the Low Temperature of the Depths of the Ocean. *Proceedings of the California Academy of Sciences,* VI (Feb. 15, 1875), 29–30.

Observations on Certain Harbor and River Improvements Collected on a Voyage from Hong-Kong, via Suez, to New York. *Report of the Superintendent of the U. S. Coast Survey . . . 1875* (App. 18), pp. 293–314. (Issued separately in 1877.)

Report on the Transit of Venus Expedition to Japan. *Ibid.* (App. 13), pp. 222–230.

Report upon the Methods Employed in Irrigating Land in India, Egypt, Italy, and Other Countries. 44th Cong., 1st sess. (1875), S. Ex. Doc. 94. 74 pp., 23 maps.

[A series of eight papers on irrigation and reclamation in Japan, China, India, Egypt, etc.; the improvement of harbors and rivers; and the breakwaters of Egypt, Italy, France, Prussia, and England.] San Francisco *Evening Bulletin,* April 7, 1876, to February 14, 1877.

Geodetic Instruments of Precision at the Paris Exposition and in European Workshops. Washington: National Academy of Sciences, 1878.

Description of the Davidson Meridian Instrument. *Report of the Superintendent of the U. S. Coast and Geodetic Survey . . . 1879* (App. 7), pp. 103–109.

The Pacific Coast and Geodetic Surveys. *California Magazine,* I (January, 1880), 60–65.

Report of the Measurement of the Yolo Base [Line], Yolo County, Cal. *Report of the Superintendent of the U. S. Coast and Geodetic Survey ... Year Ending with June, 1882* (App. 8), pp. 139–149.

Examination of the Carson Footprints. *Mining and Scientific Press,* XLVII (September 8 and 15, 1883), 150, 156.

The First Ascent of the Volcano Makushin. *Appalachia,* IV (1884), 1–11.

Collection of Some Magnetic Variations off the Coast of California and Mexico, Observed by Spanish Navigators in the Last Quarter of the Eighteenth Century. *Report of the Superintendent of the U. S. Coast and Geodetic Survey ... Year Ending with June, 1885* (App. 7), pp. 275–284.

An Examination of Some of the Early Voyages of Discovery and Exploration on the Northwest Coast of America, from 1539 to 1603. *Report of the Superintendent of the U. S. Coast and Geodetic Survey ... Year Ending with June, 1886* (App. 7), pp. 155–253. (Also issued separately.)

Submarine Valleys on the Pacific Coast of the United States. *Bulletin of the California Academy of Sciences,* II (November, 1886), 265–268.

Early Spanish Voyages of Discovery on the Coast of California. *Ibid.,* II (January, 1887), 325–335.

The Magnetic Variation at San Francisco. *Mining and Scientific Press,* January 28, 1888, pp. 52–53.

Pacific Coast. Coast Pilot of California, Oregon, and Washington. 4th ed. Washington: U. S. Coast and Geodetic Survey, 1889. 721 pp., 464 illus., 1 chart.

Report on the Measurement of the Los Angeles Base Line, Los Angeles and Orange Counties, California. *Report of the Superintendent of the U. S. Coast and Geodetic Survey ... Year Ending with June, 1889* (App. 10), pp. 217–231.

Address [at International Geodetic Association, Ninth Conference, Paris, October 3–12, 1889]. *Report of the Superintendent of the U. S. Coast and Geodetic Survey ... Year Ending with June, 1890* (App. 17), pp. 721–733.

Identification of Sir Francis Drake's Anchorage on the Coast of California in the Year 1579. San Francisco: California Historical Society, 1890. 58 pp., 15 charts.

In the Matter of the Spoliation of Yosemite Valley: Report to the Honorable Secretary of the Interior. *Annual Report of the Yosemite Commissioners,* 1890.

The Discovery of Humboldt Bay, California. *Transactions and Proceedings of the Geographical Society of the Pacific,* Vol. II, No. 1 (July, 1891). 16 pp., 5 maps. (Also issued separately.)

The Discovery of San Diego Bay. *Ibid.,* III (1892), 37–47.

The Eruption of the Volcano Weniaminof, Peninsula of Alaska. *Ibid.,* pp. 59–62.

Measurement of the Irregularity in One Turn of the Micrometer Screw, and the Relative Value of Each Turn. *Report of the Superintendent of the U. S. Coast and Geodetic Survey . . . Year Ending June 30, 1892,* Part II (App. 9), pp. 505–514.

The Occupation of Mount Conness. *Overland Monthly,* 2d ser., XIX (February, 1892), 115–129.

Early Voyages on the Northwestern Coast of America. *National Geographic Magazine,* V (1893), 235–256.

Geodesy: On the Variation of Latitude at San Francisco, Cal., from [6,768] Observations Made in Concert with the International Geodetic Association, in 1891 and 1892. *Report of the Superintendent of the U. S. Coast and Geodetic Survey . . . Year Ending June, 1893,* Part II (App. 11), pp. 441–508.

An Examination into the Genuineness of the "Jeannette" Relics; Some Evidences of Currents in the Polar Drift. San Francisco: Geographical Society of the Pacific, 1896. 16 pp.

Report to the San Francisco Committee of Commerce on the Dangers and Aids to Navigation in San Francisco Bay and the Approaches; with a Record of 349 Wrecks and Casualties. January 9, 1896. 16 pp.

Alaska. *Overland Monthly,* XXX (November, 1897), 429–439.

The Submerged Valleys of the Coast of California, U. S. A., and of Lower California, Mexico. *Proceedings of the California Academy of Sciences,* 3d ser., Geology, I (June 26, 1897), 73–104.

A Few Incidents in My Conferences with Mr. James Lick in the Matter of the Great Telescope. *University of California Magazine,* V (April, 1899), 131–137.

The Tracks and Landfalls of Bering and Chirikof on the Northwest Coast of America, from the Point of Their Separation in Latitude 49°10′, Longitude 176°40′ West, to Their Return to the Same Meridian, June, July, August, September, October, 1741. *Transactions and Proceedings of the Geographical Society of the Pacific,* 2d ser., I (1901), 1–44. (Also issued separately.)

140 ·

The Alaska Boundary. San Francisco: Alaska Packers Association, 1903.
235 pp., 2 maps.

The Glaciers of Alaska That Are Shown on Russian Charts or Mentioned
in Older Narratives. *Transactions and Proceedings of the Geographical Society of the Pacific*, 2d ser., III (1904), 1–98. (Also issued
separately.)

Points of Interest Involved in the San Francisco Earthquake. *Proceedings of the American Philosophical Society*, XLV (1906), 178–182.

The Discovery of San Francisco Bay; the Rediscovery of the Port of
Monterey; the Establishment of the Presidio, and the Founding of
the Mission of San Francisco. *Transactions and Proceedings of the
Geographical Society of the Pacific*, 2d ser., IV (1907), 1–153. (Also
issued separately.)

The Name "Mt. Rainier." *Sierra Club Bulletin*, VII (January, 1907),
87–99.

Francis Drake on the Northwest Coast of America in the Year 1579. The
Golden Hinde Did Not Anchor in the Bay of San Francisco. *Transactions and Proceedings of the Geographical Society of the Pacific*,
2d ser., V (1908), 1–114. (Also issued separately.)

The Origin and Meaning of the Name California; Calafia the Queen of
the Island of California. *Ibid.*, Vol. VI, Part 1 (1910), pp. 1–50.

· index

PORT ORFORD or EWING HARBOR

OREGON TER.

SHELTER COVE

CALIFORNIA

TIDES